CHORALE COLLECTION

Crofts Books in Music

A HISTORY OF MUSICAL THOUGHT   By D. N. Ferguson

A SHORT HISTORY OF MUSIC   By D. N. Ferguson

EASTMAN SCHOOL OF MUSIC SERIES

EXAMPLES ILLUSTRATING THE DEVELOPMENT OF MELODIC LINE AND CONTRAPUNTAL STYLE FROM GREEK MELODY TO MOZART   By Gustave Fredric Soderlund
For use in classes of Counterpoint and History of Music

EXAMPLES OF GREGORIAN CHANT AND WORKS BY ORLANDUS LASSUS, GIOVANNI PIERLUIGI PALESTRINA, AND MARC ANTONIO INGEGNERI
For use in classes of Counterpoint   By Gustave Fredric Soderlund

METHOD OF ORGAN PLAYING   By Harold Gleason
A MODERN METHOD FOR THE DOUBLE BASS   By Nelson Watson
ANSWERS TO SOME VOCAL QUESTIONS   By Thomas Austin-Ball
HANDBOOK OF CONDUCTING   By Karl Van Hoesen
CHORALE COLLECTION   By Elvera Wonderlich
Including 156 Chorales by J. S. Bach, 22 Swedish Chorales, and 20 Norwegian Chorales

SIGHT-SINGING MANUAL   By Allen Irvine McHose and Ruth Northup Tibbs
DIRECT APPROACH TO COUNTERPOINT IN SIXTEENTH CENTURY STYLE
  (*In preparation*)   By Gustave Fredric Soderlund

BASIC PRINCIPLES OF THE TECHNIQUE OF EIGHTEENTH AND NINETEENTH CENTURY COMPOSITION   By Allen Irvine McHose
  (*In preparation*)

THE HARMONIC AND CONTRAPUNTAL TECHNIQUE OF THE EIGHTEENTH AND NINETEENTH CENTURIES   By Allen Irvine McHose
  (*In preparation*)

EASTMAN SCHOOL OF MUSIC SERIES

CHORALE COLLECTION

including

156 Chorales by J. S. Bach, 22 Swedish Chorales, and 20 Norwegian Chorales

Selected and Edited by

ELVERA WONDERLICH

*Theory Department of the Eastman School of Music
of the University of Rochester*

SECOND EDITION

F. S. CROFTS & CO.
NEW YORK · · 1945

LITHOPRINTED IN UNITED STATES OF AMERICA
BY EDWARDS BROTHERS, INC., ANN ARBOR, MICHIGAN

FOREWORD

The Eastman School of Music is happy to present this publication of chorales as edited by Elvera Wonderlich of the theory department of the Eastman School of Music. This volume will prove especially valuable to the student of the technique of part-writing conceived in the period of composition in which clearly defined tonalities were dominant. There is no type of music better suited to give him technical guidance and example.

In this edition Miss Wonderlich has carefully selected and ably edited 156 Bach chorales in a manner which makes them of great practical value to the young student. The book is especially notable, however, for the inclusion of 42 Swedish and Norwegian chorales of unusual beauty. In addition to their esthetic value, these Scandinavian chorales in the stark simplicity of their harmonization form a valuable contrast to the more familiar chorales of Bach.

In this work of selecting and editing the chorales of Bach, as well as in the perhaps more difficult task of presenting outstanding examples from the field of Scandinavian chorales, Miss Wonderlich has shown evidence of the high quality of her scholarship and has contributed a volume which should be of distinct aid to every student of the art of part-writing.

Howard Hanson

Director Eastman School of Music

PREFACE

This collection of chorales is intended primarily for use in the theory classes of the Eastman School of Music. The German title of each of the chorales by Bach is usually the first line of the hymn which was most commonly associated with the chorale melody. In instances where there seems to be little or no relation between title and text, the confusion may be due to the fact that Bach has selected some stanza other than the first for that particular harmonization.

The texts for the Bach chorales have been taken from the larger works in which they occur, including the St. Matthew Passion, the St. John Passion, the Christmas Oratorio, the motet, Jesu meine Freude, and various cantatas. Those chorales, for which the words have been lost, have as texts the first stanza of the hymn of that name. Great care has been taken to provide all of the chorales with translations which are as close to the original as possible, with, it is to be hoped, some literary value.

The confusion between the vocal bass and the basso continuo, which exists in many earlier editions of Bach chorales, is avoided in this publication by giving the vocal bass only. Reference to the volume and page in the Bachgesellschaft Edition of the complete works of Bach is given with each chorale, also the name of the larger work from which the chorale is taken, the source of the hymn and the melody, and the name of the translator.

Forty-two Scandinavian chorales have been included in this collection to afford students an opportunity of becoming acquainted with Swedish and Norwegian harmonizations. The Swedish chorales are taken from Koral-Bok och Svenska messan med körer för sopran-, alt-, tenor-och bas-röster, with translations from The Hymnal and Order of Service. The Norwegian chorales are from Koralbok for den Norske Kirke, with translations from The Lutheran Hymnary. The numbers in parentheses following the Scandinavian titles refer to Koral-Bok och Svenska messan and Koralbok for den Norske Kirke.

The editor is greatly indebted to Mr. Allen I. McHose and Miss Ruth North-Northup of the Eastman School of Music for assistance in selecting the chorales; to the Rev. Felix Hanson, Dr. C. W. Fox, and Mr. William Kimmel for translations made especially for this publication; to Miss Beatrix Lien, Miss Myrtle Jensen, and Professor Per Olsson for help in finding translations for the Scandinavian chorales; and to the following publishers for permission to use texts and music:

Carl Fischer, Inc., New York, as agents of the Oxford University Press, London, for translations by C. S. Terry of Numbers 8, 17, 25, 39, 49, 52, 54, 63, 81, 88, 95, 96, 98, 100, 106, 121, 131, 132, taken from The Four-Part Chorals of J. S. Bach, edited by C. S. Terry.

G. Schirmer, Inc., New York, for translations by Charles N. Boyd and Albert Riemenschneider of Numbers 45, 66, 87, and 130, taken from Chorales by Johann Sebastian Bach, Book I, selected and edited by Charles N. Boyd and Albert Riemenschneider.

Hall & McCreary Company, Chicago, for a translation by August Crill of Number 102 taken from the Anniversary Collection of Bach Chorales by Walter E. Buszin.

The H. W. Gray Co., American agents for Novello & Co., Ltd., London, for translations by Miss H. F. H. Johnston of Numbers 71, 72, 73, and 75, taken from The Passion of Our Lord According to St. Matthew by J. S. Bach; for translations by Dr. T. A. Lacey of Numbers 21, 89, and 90, taken from The Passion of Our Lord According to St. John by J. S. Bach; for translations by J. Troutbeck of Numbers 69, 79, 126, 134, and 136, taken from The Passion of Our Lord According to St. John by J. S. Bach; for a translation by J. Troutbeck of Number 125 from The Passion of Our Lord According to St. Matthew by J. S. Bach; and for the translations by Paul England of Numbers 15 and 16, taken from the cantata Christ Lay in Death's Dark Prison by J. S. Bach.

Oliver Ditson Co., Philadelphia, for translations by John S. Dwight of Numbers 74, 76, 78, 86, 144, 145, and 152, taken from The Passion According to St. Matthew by J. S. Bach as revised and edited by Louis Koemmenich.

H. Aschehoug and Co., Oslo, Norway, for the music of the Norwegian chorales, taken from Koralbok for den Norske Kirke.

Augustana Book Concern, Rock Island, Illinois, for the music of the Swedish chorales taken from Koral-Bok och Svenska messan med körer för sopran-, alt-, tenor-och basröster; and for the translations of the Swedish chorales taken from The Hymnal and Order of Service.

Augsburg Publishing House, Minneapolis, Minnesota, for translations of the Norwegian chorales and also Numbers 6, 7, 10, and 15 of the Swedish chorales taken from The Lutheran Hymnary.

ELVERA WONDERLICH

CONTENTS

CHORALES by Johann Sebastian Bach

Page

Befiehl du deine Wege   )
O Haupt voll Blut und Wunden)   see   Herzlich thut mich verlangen
)
Gott sei uns gnädig und barmherzig,   see   Meine Seele erhebt den Herren

In allen meinen Taten   )
Nun ruhen alle Wälder   )   see   O Welt, ich muss dich lassen
O Welt, sieh hier dein Leben)

Nun lieget alles unter dir,   see   Ermuntre dich, mein schwacher Geist

Wach' auf, mein Herz,   see   Nun lasst uns Gott, dem Herren

Wär' Gott nicht mit uns diese Zeit,   see   Wo Gott der Herr nicht bei uns hält

Weg, mein Herz, mit den Gedanken,   see   Freu' dich sehr, o meine Seele

SWEDISH CHORALES

NORWEGIAN CHORALES

BIBLIOGRAPHY

Bach-Gesellschaft, J. S. BACHS WERKE, Leipzig: Bach-Gesellschaft,
    1851-1899.

Frances E. Cox, HYMNS FROM THE GERMAN, second edition, London:
    Rivingtons, 1864.

D. Albert Fischer, DAS DEUTSCHE EVANGELISCHE KIRCHENLIED, six
    volumes, Gütersloh: C. Bertelsmann, 1904-1916.

THE HYMNAL AND ORDER OF SERVICE, Rock Island: Augustana Book Con-
    cern, 1927.

John Julian, A DICTIONARY OF HYMNOLOGY, London: John Murry, 1908.

KORALBOK FOR DEN NORSKE KIRKE, Oslo: H. Aschehoug & Co., 1936.

KORAL BOK OCH SVENSKA MESSAN MED KÖRER FÖR SOPRAN-, ALT-, TENOR-,
    OCH BASRÖSTER. Rock Island: Augustana Book Concern, 1892.

James Franklin Lambert, LUTHER'S HYMNS, Philadelphia: General
    Council Publication House, 1917.

THE LUTHERAN HYMNARY, Minneapolis: Augsburg Publishing House, 1923.

Richard Massie, LUTHER'S SPIRITUAL SONGS, London: Hatchard & Co.,
    1854.

Arthur Tozer Russell, PSALMS AND HYMNS, Cambridge: Deighton, 1851.

Ludwig Schoeberlein, SCHATZ DES LITURGISCHEN CHOR-UND GEMEINDEGESANGS,
    three volumes, Göttingen: Vandenhoeck und Ruprecht, 1865-
    1872.

Charles Sanford Terry, THE FOUR-PART CHORALS OF J. S. BACH, London
    and New York: Oxford University Press, 1929.

Philipp Wackernagel, DAS DEUTSCHE KIRCHENLIED, five volumes, Leipzig:
    B. G. Teubner, 1864-1877.

Catherine Winkworth, CHORALE BOOK FOR ENGLAND, London: Longman,
    Green, Longman, Roberts, and Green, 1863.

------------LYRA GERMANICA, First and Second Series, London: Long-
    man & Co., 1855-1858.

Johannes Zahn, DIE MELODIEN DER DEUTSCHEN EVANGELISCHEN KIRCHENLIEDER,
    six volumes Gütersloh: C. Bertelsmann, 1889-1893,

CHORALES
By J. S. Bach
1-156

No. 1. ACH GOTT UND HERR, WIE GROSS UND SCHWER

(B.W. XXXIX p. 178)

Hymn by Johann Major 1613
Translation by Catherine Winkworth

Melody from As hymnodus sacer, Leipzig, 1625

Ach Gott und Herr, wie gross und schwer sind mein' be- gang- ne
A- las! my God! My sins are great, My con- science doth up-

Sün - den! Da ist Nie- mand, der hel- fen kann, in
braid me; And now I find That at my strait No

die- ser Welt zu fin- den.
man hath power to aid me.

Cantata 48 Ich elender Mensch (B.W. X p. 288)

Hymn by Johann Major 1613   Melody from As hymnodus sacer, Leipzig,1625
Translation by Catherine Winkworth

Soll's ja so   sein,   dass   Straf' und Pein auf   Sün- den   fol- gen
If   pain and woe   Must   fol- low   sin, Then be   my   path still

müs-   sen: so   fahr' hier fort und   schone   dort, und
rough-   er.   Here spare me   not; If   heaven I win, On

lass mich hier wohl bü -   -   -   -   -   -   -   -   -   -   ssen.
earth I   glad- ly   suf -   -   -   -   -   -   -   -   -   -   fer.

2

No. 3 ACH GOTT, VOM HIMMEL SIEH DAREIN

Cantata 153 Schau, lieber Gott, wie meine Feind.(B.W. XXXII p. 43)

Hymn attributed to David Denicke 1646   Melody from Erfurter Enchiridion 1524
Translation Cento

Schau', lie- ber Gott, wie mei- ne Feind'; da- mit ich stets muss
so li- stig und so mach- tig seind', dass sie mich leichtlich
Be- hold, O Lord, the many foes, With whom I struggle
'Gainst many and such mighty woes, My strenth a- vai- leth

käm- pfen, Herr, wo mich dei- ne Gnad' nicht hält, so
däm- pfen! Lord, with Thy grace my soul re- fresh! Then
ev- ney- er: vey- er.

kann der Teu- fel, Fleisch und Welt mich leicht in Un- glück
shall the De- vil, World, and Flesh No more pre- vail a-

stür- zen.
gainst me.

3

No. 4   ACH GOTT, VOM HIMMEL SIEH' DAREIN

Cantata 2 Ach Gott, vom Himmel sieh' darein (B.W. I p. 72)'

Hymn by Martin Luther 1524
Translation by Frances E. Cox

Melody from Erfurter Enchiridion 1524

Dass wollst du Gott be- wah- ren rein für diesem arg'n Ge-
Und lass uns dir be- foh- len sein, dass sich's in uns nicht
Thy truth thou wilt pre- serve, O Lord, From this vile gen- e-
Make us to lean up- on thy Word, With calm an- ti- ci-

schlech- te, der gott- los' Hauf' sich um- her find't, wo
flech- te,
ra- tion; The wicked walk on every side When,
pa- tion.

sol- che lo- se Leute sind in deinem Volk er-
'mid thy flock, the vile a- bide In power and ex- al-

ha- - - - - - ben.
ta- - - - - - tion.

4

Cantata 3 Ach Gott wie manches Herzeleid (B.W. I p. 94)

Hymn attributed to Martin Moller 1587   Melody from As hymnodus sacer 1587
Translation by J.C. Jacobi

Er- halt' mein Herz im Glau- ben rein, so   leb' und sterb' ich
Pre- serve my faith from er- ror free, That   I   may live and

dir al- lein. Je- su, mein Trost, hör' mein Be- gier': a
die in   Thee. Lord Je- sus Christ, hear my de- sire, To

mein Hei- land, wär   ich bei   dir!
praise Thee in the   heavenly choir.

No. 6   ACH GOTT WIE MANCHES HERZELEID

Cantata 153 Schau lieber Gott (B.W. XXXII p. 58)

Hymn attributed to Martin Moller 1587   Melody from As hymnodus sacer 1625
Translation by J.C. Jacobi

Drum will ich, weil ich le- be noch,
So then, as long as life shall be,

das Kreuz dir fröh- lich tra- gen nach;
I'll bear the Cross and fol- low Thee:

mein Gott mach' mich dar- zu be- reit,
O, Lord, pre- pare this heart of mine,

es dient zum Be- sten al- le- zeit.
Let it to no- thing else in- cline.

No. 7   ACH WAS SOLL ICH SÜNDER MACHEN

(B.W. XXXIX p. 179)

Hymn by Joh. Flitner 1661
Translation by Catherine Winkworth

Melody from Joh. Flitner's 'Suscitabulum musicum' 1661

Ach, was soll ich Sün- der mach- .en? ach, was soll ich
What shall I, a sin- ner do Lord? Whither shall I

fan- gen an, mein Ge- wis- sen klagt mich an,
turn for aid? Sins that make me sore a- fraid

es be- gin- net auf- zu- wachen; dies ist mei- ne
Con- science wak- ing brings to view, Lord. This my con- fi-

Zu- ver- sicht, meinen Je- sum lass' ich nicht.
d'ence shall be, Je- sus, I will cleave to Thee.

7

Cantata 112 Der Herr ist mein getreuer Hirt (B.W. XXIV p. 48)

Hymn adapted by Decius 1525
Translation by C. S. Terry   Melody from Schumann's Geistliche Lieder 1539

Gu- tes und die Barm- her- zig- keit fol- gen mir nach im
und ich werd' blei- ben al- le- zeit im Haus des Her- ren
And so, throughout my length of days His goodness faileth
And fain am I to sing His praise With- in His courts for-

Le- ben auf Erd' in christ- li- cher Gemein', und
e- ben
nev- er, His church doth us on earth sustain, And
ev- er.

nach dem Tod da werd' ich sein bei Chri- sto, mei- nem
af- ter Tod death in heaven we'll reign, From Je- sus part- ed

Her- ren.
nev- er.

8

Cantata 33 Allein zu dir, Herr Jesu Christ (B.W. Vll p. 114)

Hymn: Johann Schneesing 1542
Translation by Catherine Winkworth

Melody from Babst's Geystliche Lieder 1545

Ehr' sei Gott in dem höch- sten Thron, dem
und Jesum Christ, sein'm lieb- sten Sohn, der
Glo- ry to God in high- est Heaven. The
To His dear Son, for sin- ners giv'n, Whose

Va- ter al- zeit - - - - - ler Gü- te. und
uns all- zeit - - - - - be- hü- te.
Fa- ther of e- - - - ter- nal love; To
watch- ful grace we - - - - dai- ly prove;

Gott, dem hei- li- gen Gei- ste, der uns sein' Hülf' all-
God the Ho- ly Ghost on high: Oh, ev- er be His

9

zeit lei- ste, da- mit wir ihm ge- fäl- lig sein, hier
com- fort nigh; And teach us, free from sin and fear, To

in die- ser Zeit und fol- gends in der E- -
please - - Him here, And serve Him in the sin- -

- wig- keit.
- less sphere.

10

(B.W. XXXIX p. 182)

Hymn by Johann Heermann 1636
Translation by Elvera Wonderlich

Melody by Johann Crüger 1649

Als Je- sus Christus in der Nacht, da- rin er ward ver-
That night when Je- sus Christ, our Lord By His dis- ci- ple

ra- then, auf un- ser Heil war ganz be- dacht, das-
was be- tray'd, To us on earth He gave His Word That

selb' uns zu er- stat- ten.
ex- pi- a- tion would be made.

No. 11   AUF MEINEN LIEBEN GOTT
Cantata 5 Wo soll ich fliehen hin (B.W. I p. 150)

Hymn by Johann Heerman 1630   Melody by Johann Schein 1627
Translation anonymous

Führ auch mein Herz und Sinn   durch   dein-en Geist da-
Lord, strengthen Thou my heart; Such   grace to me im-

hin,   dass ich mög al- les mei-   den, was
part,   That nought which may a- wait   me From

mich und dich kann schei- den, und Ich an dei- nem
Thee may sep- a- rate   me; Let me with Thee, my

Lei-   be ein Gliedmass e- wig blei-   ben.
Sa-   viour, U- ni- ted be for ev-   er.

12

No. 12   AUS MEINES HERZENS GRUNDE
(B.W. XXXIX p. 184)

Hymn from Hamburg Gesangbuch 1592   Melody from Cathechismus Gesangbüchlein, Hamburg, 1598
Translation by Catherine Winkworth

Aus mei- nes Her- zens Grun- - de sag' ich dir
in die- ser Mor- gen- stun- - de dar- zu mein
My in- most heart now rais- - es, In this fair
A song of thank- ful prais- - es To Thine al-

Lob und Dank, o Gott in dei- nem Thron, dir
Le- be- lang,
morn- ing hour, And as I have be- gun This
might- y power;

zu Lob, Preis und Eh- - ren, durch Chri- stum,
day, my God, my life be Be- gun and

un- sern Her- - ren, dein' ein- ge- bor- nen Sohn.
closed with praise to Thee Through Christ, Thy only Son.

13

No. 13   AUS TIEFER NOT SCHREI' ICH ZU DIR
Cantata 38, Aus tiefer Noth schrei ich zu dir. (B.W. VII p. 300)

Hymn by Martin Luther 1524
Translation by Catherine Winkworth

Melody from Walter's Geystliche Gesangk Buchleyn 1524

Ob bei uns ist der Sün- den viel, bei Gott ist viel mehr
sein' Hand zu hel- fen hat kein Ziel, wie gross auch sei der
Though great our sins and sore our woes, His grace much more a-
His help- ing love no lim- it knows, Our ut- most need it

Gna- - de, Er ist al- lein der gu- te
Scha- - de. Our kind and faith- ful Shep- herd,
bound- - eth;
sound- - eth.

Hirt, der I- sra- el er- lö- sen wird
He, Who shall at last set Israel free

aus sei- nem Sün- den al- - len.
From all their sin and sor- - row.

14

No. 14   BEFIEHL DU DEINE WEGE
           (B.W. XXXIX p. 186)

Hymn by Paul Gerhardt 1656   Melody from Gesius'Enchiridion 1603
Translation by Frances E. Cox

Be- fiehl du dei- ne We- ge, und was dein Her- ze
der al- ler- treu- sten Pfle- ge des, der den Him- mel
To God thy way com- mend- ing, Trust Him Whose Arm of
The heav'n-ly circles bend- ing, Guides ev'ry star a-

Kränkt,   Der Wol- ken Luft und Win- den gibt
lenkt.   The winds, and clouds, and light- ning By
might,
right:

Wege, Lauf und Bahn,   der wird auch We- ge
His sure Hand are led;   And He will, dark shades

fin-   den, die   dein Fuss ge- hen   kann.
bright'- ning, Shew   Thee what path to   tread.

15

No. 15 CHRIST LAG IN TODESBANDEN

Cantata No. 4 Christ lag in Todesbanden (B.W. I P. 124)

Hymn by Martin Luther 1524
Translation by Paul England

Melody from Walter's Geystliche Gesangk Buchleyn 1524

Wir es- - sen und le- ben wohl im rech- ten O- ster-
Der al- te Sauer- teig nicht soll sein bei dem Wort der
With grateful hearts we all are met To eat the bread of
The ancient lea- ven now for- get, And ev'- ry thought of

fla- den,
Gna- den,
glad- ness.
sad- ness.

Chris- tus will die Kos- te sein und
Christ Him- self the feast hath spread, By

spei- sen die Seel' al- lein, der Glaub' will keins an-
Him the hun- gry soul is fed, And He a- lone can

dern le- ben.
feed us.

Hal- - le- lu- jah!
Hal- - le- lu- ja!

No. 16   CHRIST LAG IN TODESBANDEN

Cantata 158 Der Friede sei mit dir (B.W. XXXII 154)

Hymn by Martin Luther 1524
Translation by Paul England

Melody from Walther's Geystliche Gesangk Buchleyn 1524

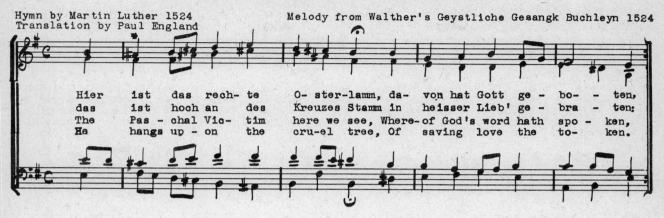

Hier ist das rech- te O- ster-lamm, da- von hat Gott ge - bo- ten,
das ist hoch an des Kreuzes Stamm in heisser Lieb' ge- bra- ten:
The Pas - chal Vic- tim here we see, Where-of God's word hath spo- ken,
He hangs up - on the cru-el tree, Of saving love the to- ken.

dess Blut zeichnet uns're Thür', dass hält der Glaub' dem
His blood ran - soms us from sin, And Death no more can

To- de für, der Wür- ger kann uns nicht rüh- ren. Hal- le- lu- ja!
on- ter in. Now Satan can- not harm - us, Hal- le- lu- jah!

\# A natural in the Bachgesellschaft Edition

17

No. 17   CHRIST UNSER HERR, ZUM JORDAN KAM

Cantata 176 Es ist ein trotzig und verzagt Ding. (B.W. XXXV p. 198)

Hymn by Paul Gerhardt 1656
Translation by C. Sanford Terry

Melody from Walter's Geystliche Gesangk Buchleyn 1524

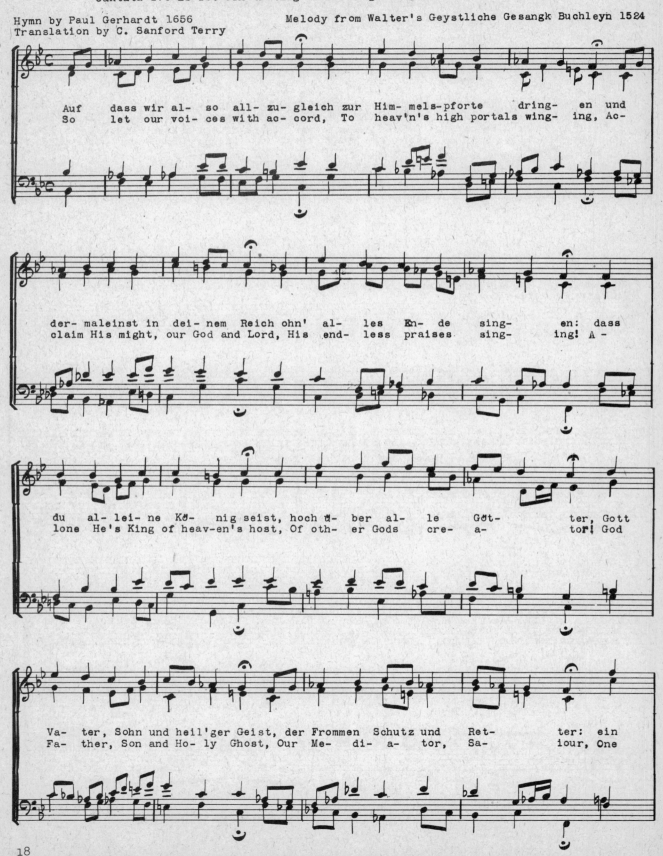

Auf dass wir al- so all- zu- gleich zur Him- mels- pforte dring- en und
So let our voi- ces with ac- cord, To heav'n's high portals wing- ing, Ac-

der- maleinst in dei- nem Reich ohn' al- les En- de sing- en: dass
claim His might, our God and Lord, His end- less praises sing- ing! A-

du al- lei- ne Kö- nig seist, hoch ü- ber al- le Gött- ter, Gott
lone He's King of heav- en's host, Of oth- er Gods cre- a- tor! God

Va- ter, Sohn und heil'ger Geist, der Frommen Schutz und Ret- ter: ein
Fa- ther, Son and Ho- ly Ghost, Our Me- di- a- tor, Sa- iour, One

We- sen, drei Per- so- nen.
God- head in Three Per- sons!

No. 18   CHRISTE, DER DU BIST TAG UND LICHT

(B.W. XXXIX p. 187)

Hymn attributed to Wolfgang Meusslin 1526   Melody from Klug's Geistliche Lieder 1535
Translation by Myles Coverdale

Chri- ste, der du bist Tag und Licht, vor dir ist, Herr, ver-bor- gen nichts; du
O   Christ, that art the light and day, The Light of Lights Thou art al- way; Thou

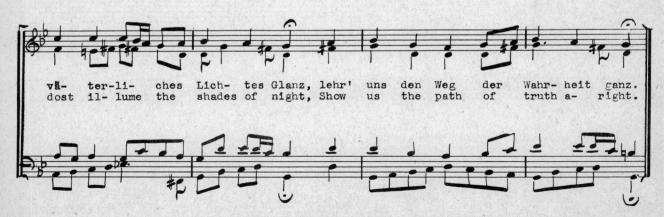

vä- ter-li- ches Lich- tes Glanz, lehr' uns den Weg der Wahr- heit ganz.
dost il- lume the shades of night, Show us the path of truth a- right.

19

No. 19   CHRISTE, DU BEISTAND DEINER KREUZGEMEINE
(B.W. XXXIX p. 187)

Hymn by Apelles von Löwenstern 1644   Melody by Appelles von Löwenstern 1644
Translation by Catherine Winkworth

No. 20   CHRISTUS DER IST MEIN LEBEN
(B.W. XXXIX p. 191)

Hymn by Melchior Vulpius 1609
Translation by Catherine Winkworth

Melody by Melchior Vulpius 1609

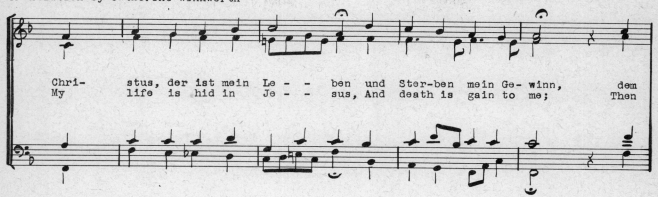

Chri- stus, der ist mein Le- - - ben und Ster-ben mein Ge- winn,   dem
My   life is hid in Je- - - sus, And death is gain to me;   Then

thu' ich mich er- ge- ben, mit Freud' fahr' ich da- hin.
when so- e'er He plea- ses, I meet it will-ing- ly.

No. 21   CHRISTUS DER UNS SELIG MACHT
St. John Passion (No. 12) B.W. XII p. 43

Hymn adapted by Michael Weisse 1531
Translation by Dr. T. A. Lacey

Melody from Calvisius'
Kirchengesenge und Geistliche Lieder 1598

Chri-stus,der uns se- lig macht,   kein Bös's hat be- gan- - gen,
He   whose life was as   the light,   Grace and truth un- sha- - ken,

der ward für uns in der Nacht als ein Dieb ge- fan- - gen
In the dark-ness of the night Like a thief was ta- - ken;

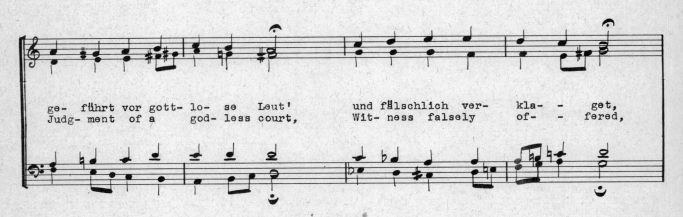

ge- führt vor gott- lo- se Leut' und fälschlich ver- kla- - get,
Judg- ment of a god- less court, Wit- ness falsely of- - fered,

ver- lacht, ver-höhnt und ver- speit, wie denn die Schrift sa- - get.
Scorn and spitting, ri- bald sport, As foretold, He suf- fered.

No. 22   CHRISTUS IST ERSTANDEN, HAT ÜBERWUNDEN

(B.W. XXXIX p. 192)

Hymn by Michael Weisse 1531
Translation by William Kimmel

Melody from Speer's Choral Gesang Buch 1692

Chri- stus ist er- stan- den, hat ü- ber- wun- den; Gnad! ist
Christ our Lord is ris- en, Now death hath He bound; Van-quished

nun vor- han- den, Wahr- heit wird fun- den. Da- rum, lie- ben
is the pris- on, And God's truth is found. Therefore Christians

Leu- te, freut euch heu- te, lo- bet eu- ren Her-
now re- joice, And with glad-some voice. Cease your singing nev-

ren, Je- sum, den Kö- nig der Eh- ren.
er, Praise to Christ the King for- ev- er.

23

No. 23 DANKET DEM HERREN, DENN ER IST SEHR FREUNDLICH

(B.W. XXXIX p. 193)

Hymn by Johann Horn 1544
Translation by Elvera Wonderlich

Tenor melody by Ludwig Senfl 1534

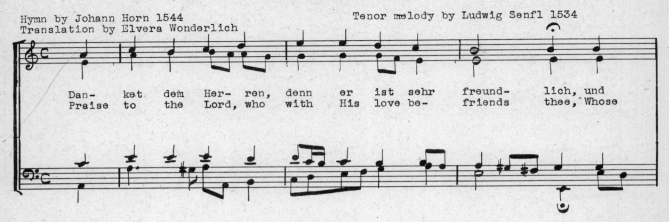

Dan- ket dem Her- ren, denn er ist sehr freund- lich, und
Praise to the Lord, who with His love be- friends thee, "Whose

sei- ne Güt' und Wahr- heit blei- bet e- wig- lich.
truth and kind- ness will en- dure e- ter- nal- ly.

No. 24   DAS ALTE JAHR VERGANGEN IST

(B.W. XXXIX p. 194)

Hymn attributed to Johannes Steuerlein 1588
Translation by J. C. Jacobi

Melody attributed to Johannes Steuerlein 1588

Das al- te Jahr ver- gan- gen ist, wir dan- ken dir, Herr
With this New Year we raise new songs To praise the Lord with

24

Je- su Christ, dass du uns in so gros- ser G'fahr be-
hearts and tongues, For His sup- port in troubles past, Where-

hü- tet hast lang' Zeit und Jahr; dass du uns in so
with our life was o- ver- cast; For His sup- port in

gros- ser G'fahr be- hü- tet hast lang' Zeit und Jahr.
trou- bles past, Where- with our life was o- ver- cast.

No. 25   DAS NEUGEBORNE KINDELEIN

Cantata 122 Das neugeborne Kindelein (B.W. XXVI p. 40)

Hymn by Cyriacus Schneegass 1597   Melody by Melchior Vulpius 1609
Translation by C. Sanford Terry

Es bringt das rech - - te Ju - bel - jahr,
Come, let us hail - - this hap-py year,

was trau- ern wir denn im-mer - dar?
And put a- way all doubt and fear,

Frisch auf! itzt ist - - es Sin- gens- zeit,
Raise our glad hearts - - to God's high throne,

das Je- su- lein - - wend't al- les Leid.
Saved by the grace - - of Christ, His Son!

DER DU BIST DREI IN EINIGKEIT
(B.W. XXXIX p. 196)

Hymn by Martin Luther 1543
Translation by Richard Massie

Melody by Hermann Schein 1627

Der   du   bist drei in Ei-   nig- keit, ein wah- rer   Gott von
Thou who art three in u-   ni- ty, True God from all e-

E-   wig- keit, die   Sonn' mit dem Tag von uns weicht, lass
ter- ni- ty,   The   sun is   fad- ing from our sight, Shine

uns leuch- ten dein   gött- lich Licht.
Thou on   us   with   heavenly light.

No. 27   DIE SONN' HAT SICH MIT IHREM GLANZ

(B.W. XXXIX p. 198)

Hymn by Josua Stegmann 1630
Translation by William Kimmel

Melody from French Psalm Book 1542

Die   Sonn' hat sich mit ih- rem Glanz ge- wen- det und,
The   fad- ing sun has from the heav'ns de- scend- ed, Its

was   sie soll, auf die- sen Tag voll- en- det; die
rad- iant glow, that was the day has end- ed. Night's

dun- kle Nacht dringt al- lent- hal- ben zu, bringt Menschen,
shad- ows move se- rene- ly to the West, And bring to

Vieh und al- le Welt zur Ruh'.
man and all the world, sweet rest.

Hymn by Martin Luther 1524
Translation by Richard Massie

Melody from Erfurt Enchiridion 1524

Diess sind die heil'- gen zehn Ge- bot', die uns gab un- ser
That man a God- ly life might live, God did these ten com-

Her- re Gott durch Mo- se, sei- nen Die- ner treu, hoch
mand- ments give By his true ser- vant, Mos- es, high Up-

auf dem Berg Si- na- i. Ky- rie e- leis!
on the mount Si- na- i Have mer- cy, Lord.

29

No. 29   DIR, DIR, JEHOVA, WILL ICH SINGEN

(B.W. XXXIX p. 199)

Hymn by Bartholomäus Crasselius 1697
Translation by Catherine Winkworth

Melody by J. S. Bach 1736

Dir, dir, — Je— ho— va, — will — ich sin— gen,
Dir will — ich meine Lie— der brin— gen;
Je— ho— — vah let me now a— dore Thee,
With songs — I fain would come — be— fore Thee;

denn wo ist doch ein sol— cher Gott, wie du?
ach gib mir dei— nes Gei— stes Kraft dar— zu,
For where is there a God, such, Lord, as Thou?
Oh let Thy Spirit deign to teach me now

dass ich — es thu' im Na— men Je— su
To praise — Thee in His name, through whom a—

30

Christ, so wie es dir durch ihn ge-fäl-lig ist.
lone Our songs can please Thee, Through Thy bless-ed Son.

No. 30   DU FRIEDEFÜRST, HERR JESU CHRIST.
Cantata 67 Halt' im Gedächtniss Jesum Christ (B.W. XVI 246)

Hymn by Jacob Ebert 1601   Melody by Bartholomäus Gesius 1601
Translation by Catherine Winkworth

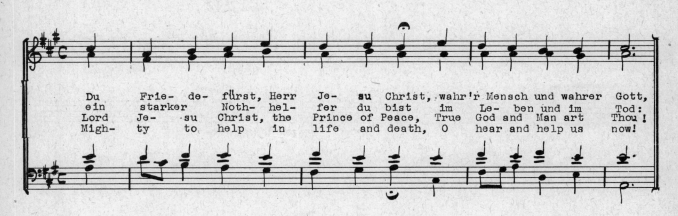

Du Frie-de-fürst, Herr Je-su Christ, wahr'r Mensch und wahrer Gott,
ein starker Noth-hel-fer du bist im Le-ben und im Tod:
Lord Je-su Christ, the Prince of Peace, True God and Man art Thou!
Migh-ty to help in life and death, O hear and help us now!

drum wir al-lein im Na-men dein zu dei-nem Va-
'Tis through Thy name a-bove we claim The mer-cy of

31

-Thy -ter schrei- en.
Thy -Fa- ther!

No. 31   DU GROSSER SCHMERZENSMANN

(B.W. XXXIX p. 199)

Hymn by Adam Thebesius c. 1652   Melody by M. Janus 1663
Translation by Elvera Wonderlich

Du   gross- er Schmerzens- mann,   vom Va- ter so ge-
In   sor- row Thou, o   Lord   didst suf- fer sore chas-

schla- gen,   Herr Je- su, dir sei Dank   für
tise- ment.   Thanks be to Thee, O Lord   For

32

al- le dei ne Pla- gen: für dei ne See- len-
ev- 'ry pain and tor- ment, For a- go- ny and

angst, für dei ne Band' und Noth, für
woe And ev'- ry tor- tured breath Thou

dei ne Geis- se- lung, für dei nen bittern Tod.
suf- fered here be- low, And for Thy cru- el death.

33

Cantata 18 Ich will den Kreuzstab gerne tragen (B.W. XII² 104)

Hymn by Johann Franck 1649   Melody by Johann Crüger 1649
Translation by Catherine Winkworth

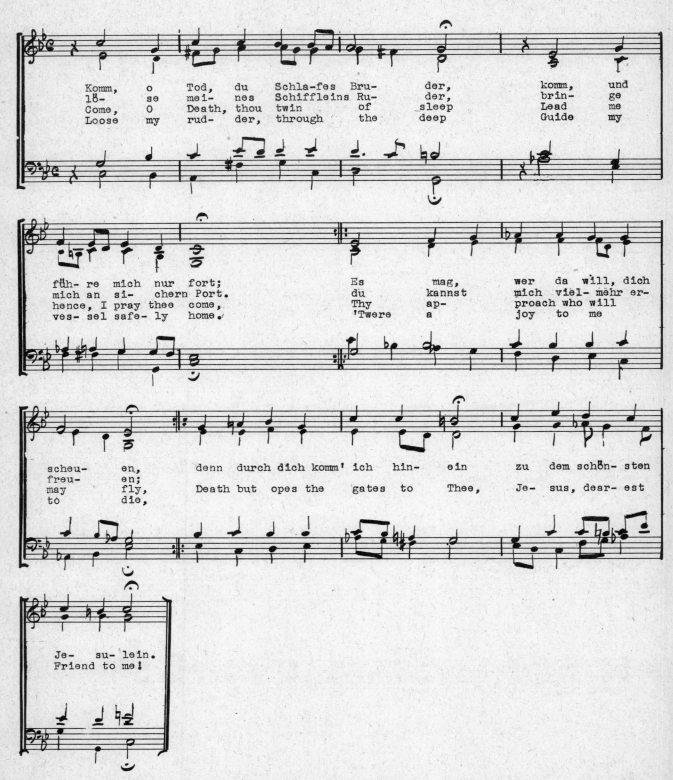

Komm, o Tod, du Schla-fes Bru- der,   komm, und brin- ge
18- se mei- nes Schiffleins Ru- der,   brin- ge
Come, O Death, thou twin of sleep   Lead me
Loose my rud- der, through the deep   Guide my

füh- re mich nur fort;   Es mag,   wer da will, dich
mich an si- chern Port.   du kannst mich viel- mehr er-
hence, I pray thee come,   Thy ap-   proach who will
ves- sel safe- ly home.   'Twere a   joy to me

scheu- en,   denn durch dich komm' ich hin- ein zu dem schön- sten
freu- en;   Death but opes the gates to Thee, Je- sus, dear- est
may fly,   to die,

Je- su- lein.
Friend to me!

34

No. 33   DU, O SCHÖNES WELTGEBÄUDE

(B.W. XXXIX p. 200)

Hymn by Johann Franck 1649
Translation by Catherine Winkworth

Melody by Johann Crüger 1649

Cantata 18 Gleich wie der Regen und Schnee (B.W. II p. 252)

Hymn by Lazarus Spengler 1524   Melody from Klug's Geistliche Lieder 1535
Translation by J.C. Jacobi

Ich   bitt' o   Herr, aus Her-   zens Grund, du wollst nicht von   mir
dein   heil'ges Wort aus mei-   nem Mund; so   wird   mich   nicht   be-
I   send my   cries un- to   the Lord; My   heart im-   plores His
To   grant me of His liv- ing Word A   nev-   er-   fail- ing

neh-   men   mein' Sünd und Schuld, denn in   dein' Huld setz'
schä   men,
fa-   vor: That   sin and shame May   lose the   claim To
sa-   vor;

ich   all   mein Ver- trau- en, Wer   sich   nur   fest da-
hin- der   my sal- va-   tion; In   Christ, the   scope Of

rauf ver- lässt, der wird den Tod nicht schau-   -   en.
all my   hope, I   'scape death and dam- na-   -   tion.

Cantata 80 Ein' feste Burg ist unser Gott. (B.W. XVIII p. 378)

Hymn by Martin Luther 1527   Melody by Martin Luther 1527
Translation by Catherine Winkworth

(B.W. XXXIX 202)

Hymn by Erhart Hagenwalt 1524   Melody from Walter's Geystliche gesangk Buchleyn 1524
Translation by J.C. Jacobi

Er-   barm' dich mein, o   Her-   re   Gott,   nach
wasch' ab;   mach' rein mein' Mis-   se-   that,   ich
Show   pi-   ty,   Lord! O   cies   large   for-   give!   Let
Are   not   thy   mer- cies large   and   free?   May

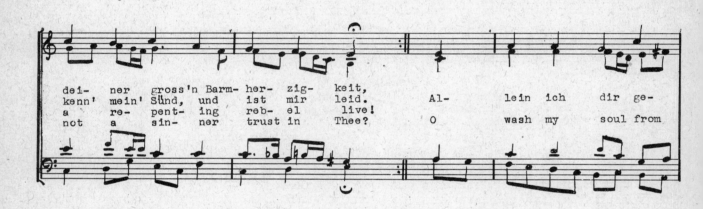

dei-   ner   gross'n Barm- her- zig- keit,   Al-   lein ich   dir ge-
kenn' mein' Sünd, und   ist   mir   leid.   O   wash my   soul from
not   a   sin-   ner   trust in   Thee?

sün-   digt hab, das ist wi- der mich ste- tig- lich; das
ev-   'ry   sin, And make my   guil-ty con- science clean; Here

Bös' vor dir nicht mag be-stah'n, du bleibst- ge-
on my heart the bur-den lies, And past--- of-

recht, ob man ur- thei- le dich.
fen- ces pain ur- mine le eyes.

No. 37   ERHALT' UNS HERR, BEI DEINEM WORT

Cantata 6 Bleib bei uns, denn es will Abend werden. (B.W. I p. 176)

Hymn by Martin Luther 1541   Melody from Klug's Geistliche Lieder 1535
Translation by Catherine Winkworth

Be- weis' dein' Macht, Herr Je- su Christ, der
Lord Je- sus Christ, Thy pow'r make known, For

du   Herr   al -   ler   Her-   ren bist: be- schirm' dein' ar- me
Thou   art   Lord   of   lords a-   lone; De- fend Thy   Christen-

Chris-   ten-   heit,   dass   sie   dich lob' in   E-   wig-   keit.
dom,   that   we   May   ev-   er- more sing   praise to   Thee.

No. 38   ERMUNTRE DICH, MEIN SCHWACHER GEIST

Christmas Oratorio (B.W. V^2 p. 59)

Hymn by Johann Rist 1641   Melody by Johann Schop 1641
Translation by J. Troutbeck

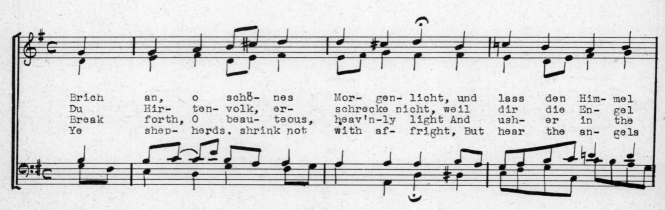

Brich   an,   o schö- nes   Mor- gen- licht, und   lass   den Him- mel
Du   Hir-   ten- volk, er- schrecke nicht, weil   dir   die En- gel
Break   forth, O beau- teous, heav'n-ly light And   ush-   er in the
Ye   shep- herds, shrink not with af- fright, But   hear   the an- gels

ta- gen!
sa- gen: dass die- ses schwache Knäbe- - lein soll
morn- ing; This Child, now weak in in- fan- cy, Our
warn- ing.

un- ser Trost und Freu- de sein, da- zu den Sa- tan
con- fi- dence and joy shall be, The pow'r of Sa- tan

zwin- gen und letzt- lich Frie- den brin- gen.
break- ing, Our peace e- ter- nal mak- ing.

41

No. 39   ERMUNTRE DICH, MEIN SCHWACHER GEIST

Cantata 11 Lobet Gott in seinen Reichen (B.W. II, p. 32)

Hymn by Johann Rist 1641
Translation by C.S. Terry

Melody by Johann Schop 1641

42

Was- ser,   Feu'r   und   Er-   den   muss
heav- en,   fire,   and   o-   cean   Lie

dir   zu Dien- ste wer-   den.
pros-   trate in de- vo-   tion.

No. 40   ERSCHIENEN IST DER HERRLICH' TAG

Cantata 67 Halt im Gedächtniss Jesum Christ (B.W. XVI p. 233)

Hymn by Nicolaus Herman 1560   Melody by Nicolaus Herman 1560
Translation by Elvera Wonderlich

Er-   schie- nen   ist   der   herr-   lich'
The   day   hath   dawn'd, the   day   of

Tag, d'ran sich Nie- mand g'nug freu- en
days, So let us sing our fer- vent

mag: Christ, un- ser Herr, heut' tri- um-
praise, For Christ, our Lord, has tri- umphed to-

phirt, all' sein' Feind' er ge- fangen
day; His en- e- mies are cast a-

führt. Al- le- lu- ja!
way. Al- le- lu- ja!

Cantata 145 So du mit deinem Mund. (B.W. XXX p. 122)

Hymn by Nicolaus Herman 1560
Translation by Catherine Winkworth

Melody by Nicolaus Herman 1560

Drum wir auch bil- lig fröh- lich sein,
With all Thy saints, Thee, Lord, we sing,

sin- gen das Hal- le- lu- ja fein, und
Praise, hon- our, thanks to Thee we bring, That

lo- ben dich, Herr Je- su Christ; zu
Thou, O long ex- pect- ed guest, Hast

Trost du uns er- stan- den bist. Hal- le- lu- ja!
come at last to make us blest! Hal- le- lu- ja!

Cantata 86 Wahrlich, ich sage euch. (B.W. XX¹ p. 134)

Hymn by Paulus Speratus 1523   Melody from Etlich Christliche Lyeder 1524
Translation by Henry Mills

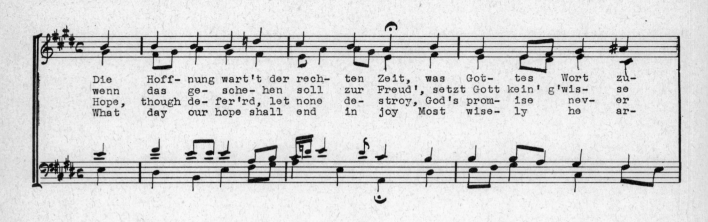

Die Hoff- nung wart't der rech- ten Zeit, was Got- tes Wort zu se-
wenn das ge- sche- hen soll zur Freud', setzt Gott kein' g'wis- se
Hope, though de- fer'd, let none de- stroy, God's prom- ise nev- er
What day our hope shall end in joy Most wise- ly he ar-

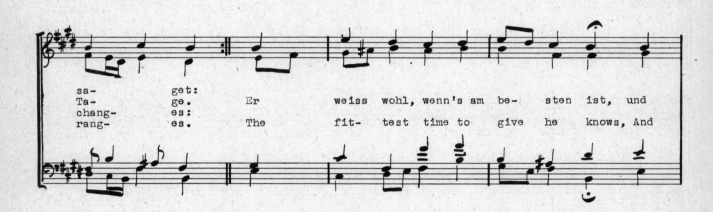

sa- get:
Ta- ge. Er weiss wohl, wenn's am be- sten ist, und
chang- es: The fit- test time to give he knows, And
rang- es.

braucht an uns kein' ar- ge List, dess soll'n wir ihm ver- trau- en.
how that know- ledge to dis- close, With Him we well may leave it.

No. 43   ES IST DAS HEIL UNS KOMMEN HER

Cantata 9 Es ist das Heil uns kommen her. (B.W. I p. 274)

Hymn by Paulus Speratus 1523
Translation by J.C. Jacobi

Melody from Etlich Christliche Lyeder 1524

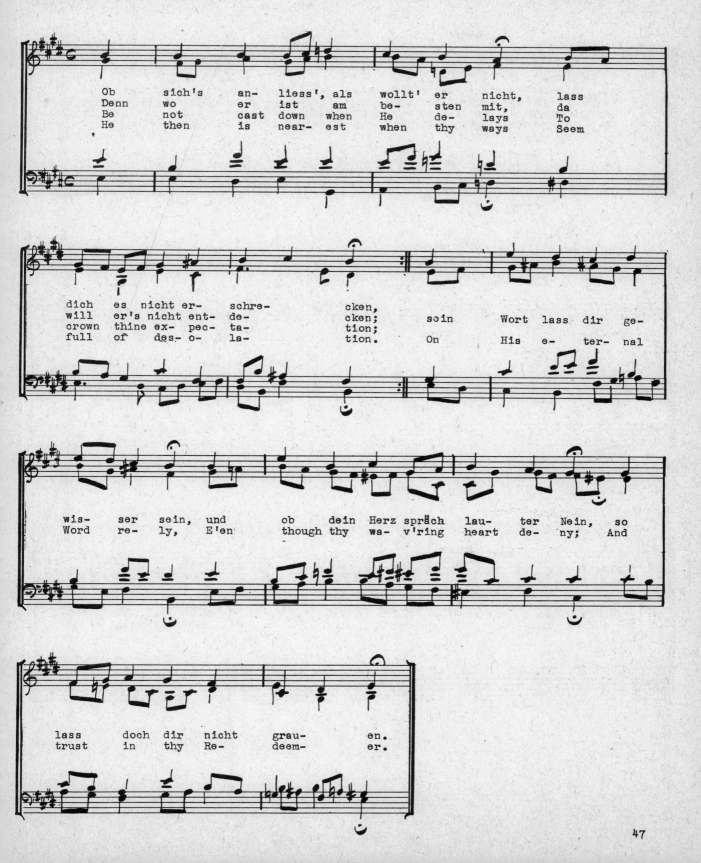

Ob sich's an liess', als wollt' er nicht, lass
Denn wo er ist am be- sten mit, da
Be not cast down when He de- lays To
He then is near- est when thy ways Seem

dich es nicht er- schre- cken, sein Wort lass dir ge-
will er's nicht ent- de- cken; son Wort lass dir ge-
crown thine ex- pec- ta- tion; On His e- ter- nal
full of des- o- la- tion. On His e- ter- nal

wis- ser sein, und ob dein Herz sprach lau- ter Nein, so
Word re- ly, E'en though thy wa- v'ring heart de- ny; And

lass doch dir nicht grau- en.
trust in thy Re- deem- er.

47

Cantata 155 Mein Gott, wie lang', ach lange. (B.W. XXXII p. 96)

Hymn by Paulus Speratus 1523
Translation by J.C. Jacobi

Melody from Etlich Christliche Lyeder 1524

Ob   sich's an-   liess', als   wollt' er   nicht, lass
denn   wo   er   ist   am   be-   sten   mit,   da
Be   not   cast down   when   He   de-   lays   To
He   then   is   near-   est,   when   thy   ways   Seem

dich   es   nicht er-   schre- cken,
will   er's   nicht ent-   de-   cken;   sein   Wort   lass   dir   ge-
crown thine ex-   pec-   ta-   tion.
full   of   des-   o-   la-   tion.   On   His   e-   ter- nal

wis-   ser   sein,   und   ob   dein   Herz   spräch' lau- ter Nein, so
Word   re-   ly,   E'en   though thy   wa-   v'ring   heart de- ny;   And

lass   doch   dir   nicht   grau-   en.
trust in   thy   re-   deem-   er.

Cantata 60 O Ewigkeit, du Donnerwort (B.W. XII² p. 190)

Hymn by Franz Burmeister 1662
Translation by Charles N. Boyd

Melody by Johann Ahle 1662

Es ist ge- nug: Herr, wenn es dir ge- fällt, so
It is e- nough! Lord, by Thy wise de- cree I

span- ne mich doch aus. Mein Jesus kommt: nun gu- te
gird me to de- part. My Jesus comes! Fare-well, O

Nacht, o Welt! ich fahr' in's Him- mels- haus, ich fah- re
world, to thee; I seek my heav'n- ly home. In peace I

sich- er hin mit Frie- den, mein gros- ser
trav- el sure- ly on- ward; Be- hind is

Jam- mer bleibt dar- nie- den. Es ist ge-
earth- ly grief and sor- row; It is e-

nug, es ist ge- nug.
nough, it is e- nough!

Christmas Oratorio (B.W. v² p. 245)

Hymn by Paul Gerhardt 1653   Melody from Klug's Geistliche Lieder 1535
Translation by J. Troutbeck

No. 47   ES SPRICHT DER UNWEISEN MUND

(B.W. XXXIX p. 204)

Hymn by Martin Luther c. 1518   Melody from Walter's Geystliche gesangk Buchleyn 1524
Translation by Richard Massie

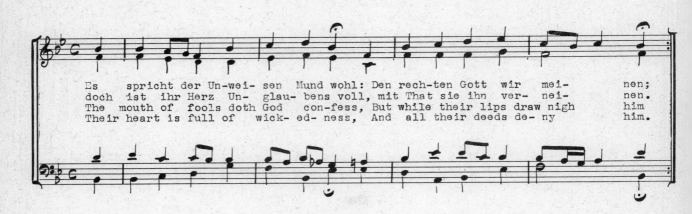

Es   spricht der Un-wei- sen Mund wohl: Den rech-ten Gott wir mei-   nen;
doch ist ihr Herz Un- glau- bens voll, mit That sie ihn ver- nei-   nen.
The mouth of fools doth God con-fess, But while their lips draw nigh him.
Their heart is full of wick- ed- ness, And all their deeds de- ny him.

Ihr   We- sen ist ver- der- bet zwar, für   Gott ist es ein
Cor- rupt are they, and ev- 'ry one A-   bom- i- na- ble

Greu- el gar, es thut Ihr' Kei- ner kein   Gut.
deeds hath done; There is not one well- do-   er.

52

No. 48   ES STEH'N VOR GOTTES THRONE

(B.W. XXXIX p. 204)

Hymn by Ludwig Helmbold 1585   Melody from Burck's Dreissig Geistliche Lieder 1594
Translation by Elvera Wonderlich

Es steh'n vor Got- tes Thro- ne, es steh'n vor Got- tes
der in sei'm lie- ben Soh- ne, der in sei'm lie- ben
Be- fore God's throne in heav- en, Be- fore God's throne in
God's Son to us was giv- en, God's Son to us was

Thro- ne, die un- sre Wäch- ter sind, dass
Soh- ne liebt al- ler Men- schen Kind,
heav- en, Our guard- ian an- gels wait.
giv- en, To save man- kind from hate. God

er auch nicht der Ei- nes ver- acht' will hab'n so
cares for all the weak- est, De- spis- es not the

Klei- nes, als je- mals ist ge- bor'n, als je- mals ist ge- bor'n.
meek- est That e'er on earth was born, That e'er on earth was born.

53

Hymn by Michael Weisse 1531
Translation by C.S. Terry

Melody by Michael Weisse 1531

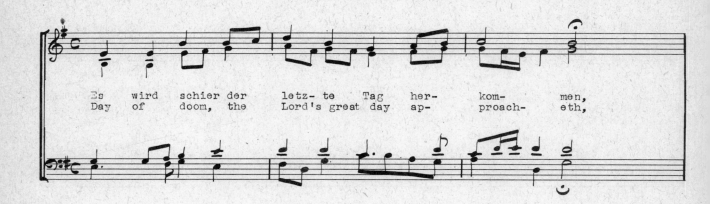

Es   wird   schier der   letz- te   Tag   her-   kom-   men,
Day   of   doom, the   Lord's great day ap-   proach-   eth,

denn   die Bos- heit   hat   sehr zu- ge- nom-   men;
When   to   judge the   world in   wrath He   com-   eth.

was   Chri- stus hat   vor ge-   sagt,   das wird jetzt be- klagt.
Lo,   the   hour that   Christ did   tell   Calls to heav'n or hell!

54

(B.W. XXXIX p. 205)

Hymn by Martin Luther 1524
Translation by Arthur Tozer Russell

Melody from Strassburger Kirchenamt 1525

Es woll' uns Gott ge-nä - - - dig sein und
sein Ant-litz uns mit hel - - - lem Schein er-
May God un-to us gra - - - cious be, And
Lord show Thy face un-to us through Thee E-

sei - nen Se - gen ge - - - - ben;   dass
leucht' zum ew'-gen Le - - - ben,   dass
grant to us His bless- - - ing;   That
ter-nal life pos-sess- - - ing: That

wir er-ken-nen sei - ne Werk' und, was ihn liebt, auf
all Thy work and will, O God, To us may be re-

Er- veal-   den,   und   Je- sus Chri- stus   Heil und Stärk' be-
    ed,   And   Christ's sal- va- tion   spread a- broad To

kannt den Hei- den   wer-   den und   sie   zu Gott be-
hea- then lands un-   seal-   ed, And   un- to God con-

keh-   ren.
vert   them.

Cantata 69 Lobe den Herrn, meine Seele (B.W. XVI p. 325)

Hymn by Martin Luther 1524   Melody from Strassburger Kirchenamt 1525
Translation by Arthur Tozer Russell

Es dan-ke, Gott, und lo- - -be dich   das
Land bringt Frucht und bes- - -sert sich,   dein
Thy fold, O God, shall bring - -to Thee   The
word shall rich-ly fruit- -. ful be,   And

Volk in gu-ten Tha- - - -ten.   Das
Wort ist wohl ge-ra- - -ing;   Thy
praise of ho-ly liv- - -   then. Uns
earth shall yield thanks-giv- - -ing. Bless

seg- ne Va-ter und der Sohn, uns seg- ne Gott, der
us, O Fa-ther! bless, O Son! Grant, Ho-ly Ghost, Thy

* (Chord third appears in instrumental accompaniment)

heil'- ge Geist, dem al- le Welt die Eh- re thu', vor
bless- - ing! Thee earth shall hon- or-- Thee a- lone, Thy

ihm sich fürch- te al- ler- meist, und
fear all souls pos- sess- - ing. Now

sprecht von Her- zen: A- - men!
let our hearts say, A- - men.

Cantata 19 Es erhub sich ein Streit (B. W. II p. 288)

Hymn from Demantius's Threnodiae 1620   Melody from French Psalter 1551
Translation by C. Sanford Terry

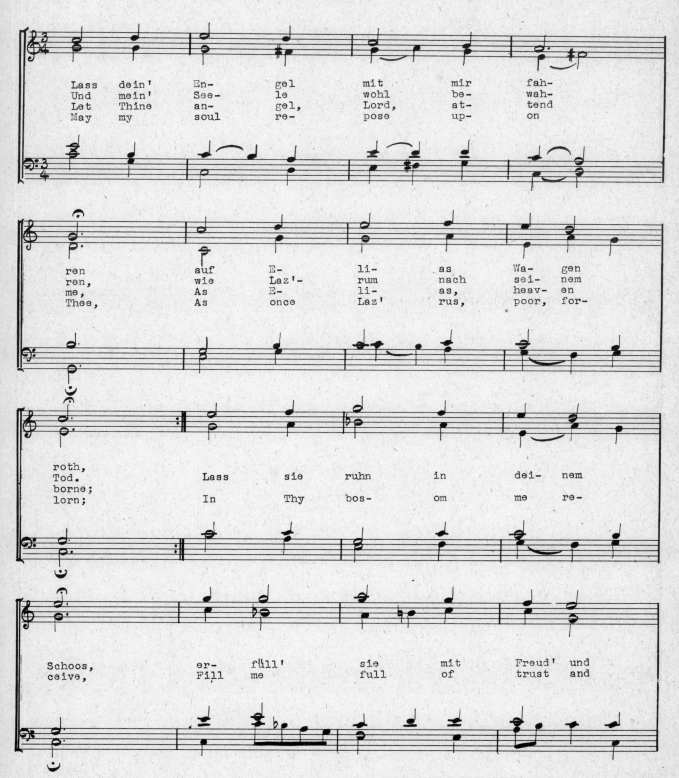

Trost,   bis   der   Leib   kommt   aus   der
love,   Till   my   ris-   en   soul   and

Er-   de,   und   mit   ihr   ver-
bo-   dy   Both   u-   nite   a-

ei-   nigt   wer-   de.
bove   in   glo-   ry!

* (Chord third appears in instrumental accompaniment)

No. 53   FREU' DICH SEHR, O MEINE SEELE

Cantata 25 Es ist nichts Gesundes an meinem Leibe (B.W. V¹ p. 188)

Hymn by Johann Heermann 1630
Translation by C. Sanford Terry

Melody from French Psalter 1551

Cantata 39 Brich dem Hungrigen dein Brod (B.W. VII p. 348)

Hymn by David Denicke c. 1648   Melody from French Psalter 1551
Translation by C. Sanford Terry

Se-   lig sind, die aus Er- bar- men   sich an-   neh- men
sind mit-lei- dig mit den Ar- men,   bit- ten   treu- lich
Blest are they whose founts of mer- cy   Free- ly   for an-
To   the poor their alms dis-burse they, Pray-ing   God to

from- der Noth,
für sie Gott.   Die be- hülf- lich sind mit Rath,
oth- er flow,
heal their woe.   Who the help-less aids with word,

auch, wo mög- lich, mit der That,   wer- den wie- se der
Or   to gen- 'rous acts is stirred, Shall him-self God's

Hülf em- pfan-   gen,   und Barm- her- zig- keit er- lan- gen.
hand be giv-   en,   Stretched to lead him up to heav- en.

62

Cantata 40 Dazu ist erschienen der Sohn Gottes (B.W. VII p. 394)

Hymn by Christian Keimann 1646   Melody from Hammerschmidt's Musicalische Andachten 1646
Translation by Catherine Winkworth

Je- su, nimm dich dei- ner Glie- der fer- ner in Ge-
Je- su, guard and guide Thy mem- bers, Fill Thy breth- 'ren

na- den an; schen- ke, was man bit- ten kann,
with Thy grace, Hear their pray'rs in ev- 'ry place,

zu er- qui- cken dei- ne Brü- der: gieb der gan- zen
Quick- en now life's faint- est em- bers; Grant all Chris- tians,

63

Chris- ten- schaar, Frie- den und ein sel'- ges Jahr!
far and near, Ho- ly peace, a glad New Year!

Freu- de, Freu- de ü- ber Freu- de! Chri- stus wehr- et
Joy, O joy be- yond all glad- ness! Christ hath done a-

al- lem Lei- de. Won- ne, Won- ne ü- ber Won- ne!
way with sad- ness! Hence, all sor- row, all re- pin- ing,

er ist die Ge- na- den- son- ne.
For the Sun of grace is shin- ing.

FÜR FREUDEN LASST UNS SPRINGEN

(B.W. XXXIX p. 206)

Hymn by Casperl Peltsch 1648
Translation by Elvera Wonderlich

Melody from Riemann's Sammlung
alter und neuer Melodien 1747

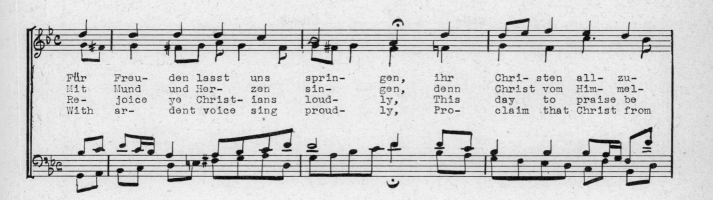

Für Freu- den lasst uns sprin- gen, ihr Chri- sten all- zu-
Mit Mund und Her- zen sin- gen, denn Christ vom Him- mel-
Re- joice ye Christ- ians loud- ly, This day to praise be
With ar- dent voice sing proud- ly, Pro- claim that Christ from

glei- che!
rei- chen che von ei- ner Jung- frau ist ge- bor'n, wer
giv- en;
heav- en Is born this day in Beth- le- hem, Pro-

hat zu- vor ge- hört von sol- chen Din- gen?
claim to all on earth This won- drous sto- ry.

Cantata 64 Sehet, welch' eine Liebe (B.W. XVI p. 118)

Hymn by Martin Luther 1524   Melody from Walter's Geistliche gesangk Buchleyn 1524
Translation by Richard Massie

Das   hat er Al- les uns ge- than,   sein' gross' Lieb' zu zei- gen an. Dess
All   this He did that He might prove To us sin- ners His great love; For

freu' sich al-   le Chri- sten- heit und   dank! ihm   dess   in
'this let Chris- ten- dom a-   dore. And   praise His   name for-

E- wig- keit. —   —   Ky- rie- leis!
ev- er- more. —   —   Ky- rie- leis.

66

Hymn by Martin Luther 1524   Melody from Walter's Geistliche gesangk Buchleyn 1524
Translation by Richard Massie

Ge- lo- bet seist du,   Je- su Christ, dass du Mensch ge- bo- ren bist, von
All praise, Lord, Je-sus Christ, to Thee, Who con- de- scendest man to be! Of

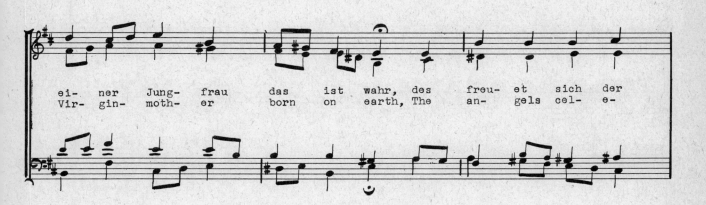

ei- ner Jung- frau   das   ist wahr, des   freu- et sich der
Vir- gin- moth- er   born   on earth, The   an- gels cel- e-

En-   - gel Schar.   Al- le- lu-   ja!
brate   Thy   -   birth. Al- le- lu-   ja!

No. 59   GELOBET 'SEIST DU, JESU CHRIST

Christmas Oratorio (B.W. v² p. 110)

Hymn by Martin Luther 1524   Melody from Walter's Geistliche gesangk Buchleyn 1524
Translation by J. Troutbeck

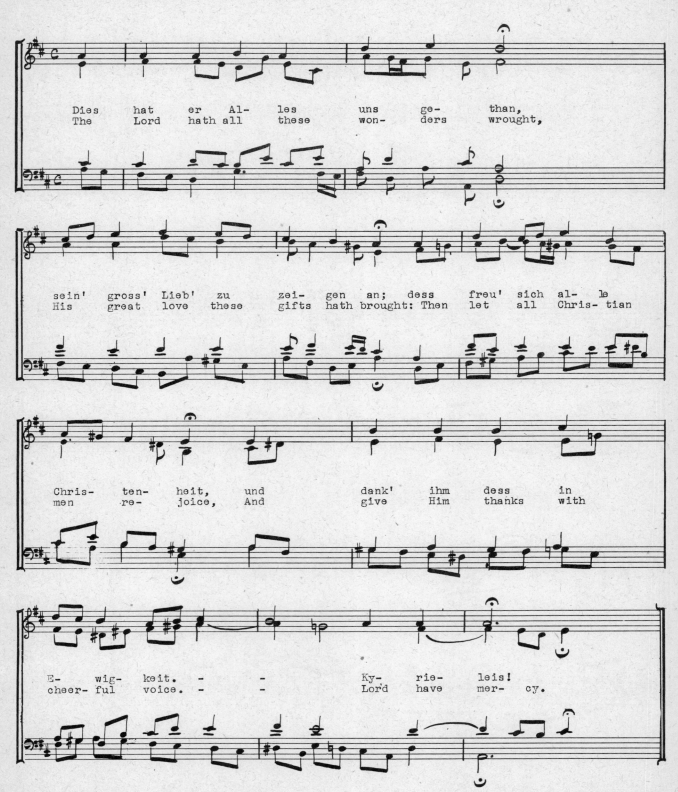

Dies hat er Al- les   uns ge-   than,
The   Lord hath all these won- ders   wrought,

sein' gross' Lieb' zu   zei- gen an; dess freu' sich al- le
His   great love these gifts hath brought: Then let all Chris- tian

Chris- ten- heit, und   dank' ihm dess   in
men re- joice, And   give Him thanks with

E-   wig- keit. —   Ky- rie- leis!
cheer- ful voice. — —   Lord have mer- cy.

68

Hymn by Heinrich Alberti 1643
Translation by J. Troutbeck

Melody by Heinrich Alberti 1642

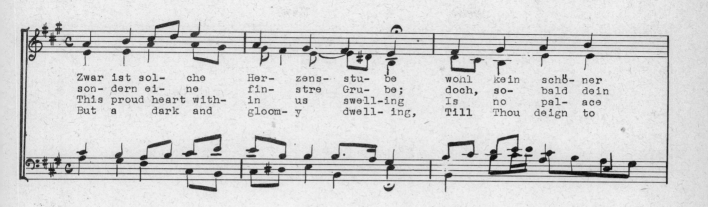

Zwar ist sol- che Her- zens- stu- be; wohl kein schö- ner
son- dern ei- ne fin- stre Gru- be; doch, so- bald dein
This proud heart with- in us swell- ing Is no pal- ace
But a dark and gloom- y dwell- ing, Till Thou deign to

Für- sten- saal, in die- sel- be nur wird blin- ken,
Gna- den- strahl
rich and fair, When Thy grace with- in it beam- eth,
en- ter there.

wird sie vol- ler Son- nen dün- ken.
Full of heav'n- ly light it seem- eth.

69

Hymn by Erasmus Alberus 1548
Translation by C. Warren Fox

Melody by Erasmus Alberus 1549

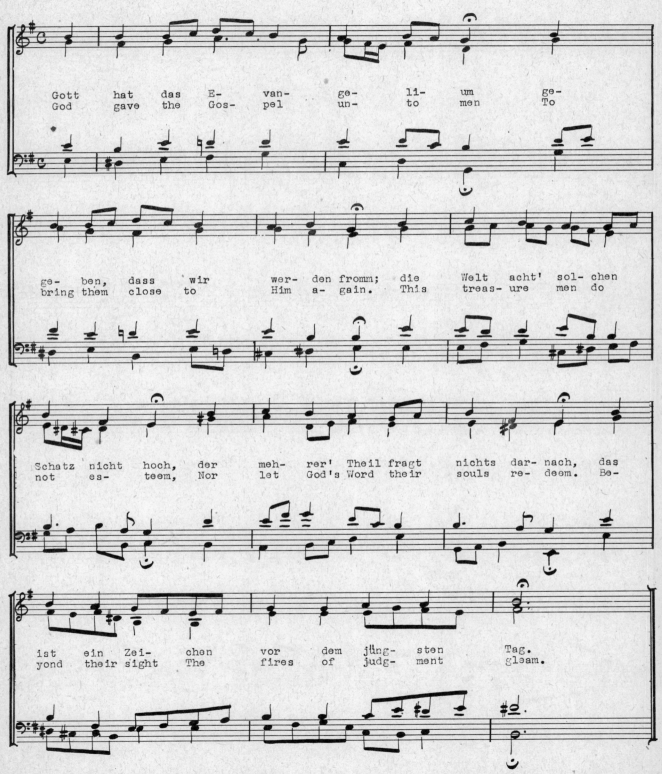

Gott   hat   das   E-   van-   pel   ge-   li-   um   ge-
God   gave   the   Gos-   pel   un-   to   men   To

ge-   ben,   dass   wir   wer-   den fromm;   die   Welt   acht'   sol- chen
bring them close to   Him a- gain.   This   treas- ure   men do

Schatz nicht hoch,   der   meh- rer' Theil fragt   nichts dar- nach, das
not es- teem,   Nor   let   God's Word their   souls re- deem. Be-

ist   ein Zei-   chen   vor   dem jüng- sten   Tag.
yond their sight The   fires of judg- ment   gleam.

70

No. 62   GOTT SEI GELOBET UND GEBENEDEIET

(B.W. XXXIX p. 211)

Hymn by Martin Luther 1524   Melody from Walter's Geistliche gesangk Buchleyn 1524
Translation by Richard Massie

Gott   sei   ge- lo-   bet   und   ge-   be-   ne-   dei-
mit   sei- nem Flei- sche   und   mit   sei-   nem   Blu-
May   God   be prais'd hence-forth and   blest for- ev-
With   his   own flesh   and   blood our   souls doth nour-

et,   der uns   sel- ber hat ge- spei-   set
te;   das gib   uns, Herr Gott, zu Gu-   te!
er!   Who, him- self both gift and giv-   er,
ish;   May they   grow there-by and flour-   ish!

Ky-   rie   e- lei-   -   -   son. Herr, durch dei- nen
Ky-   rie   e- lei-   -   -   son. By   Thy   ho- ly

71

heil' gen Leich- nam, der von dei- ner Mutt'r Ma-
bo- dy, Lord, the same Which from Thine own moth- er

ri- a kam, und das hei- li- ge Blut
Ma- ry came By the drops Thou didst bleed,

hilf uns Herr, aus al- ler Noth.
Help us in the hour of need!

Ky- rie e-
Ky- rie e-

lei- - - - son.
lei- - - - son.

Cantata 96 Herr Christ, der einig Gott's Sohn (B.W. XXII p. 184)

Hymn by Elizabeth Cruciger 1524   Melody from Erfurt Enchiridion 1524
Translation by Myles Coverdale

Er-den tödt' uns durch dein' Gü- te, er- weck' uns durch dein'
den al- ten Men- schen krän- ke, dass der neu' le- ben
A- wake us, Lord, we pray Thee; Thy ho- ly Spirit us

Gnad';
mag wohl hier auf die- ser Er- den, den
give. So will we al- ways thank Thee, That

Sinn und all' Be- gehr- en und G'dan- ken hab'n zu dir.
show'st us so great mer- cy, And our sons dost for- give.

73

No. 64   HERR GOTT, DICH LOBEN ALLE WIR

(B.W. XXXIX p. 213)

Hymn adapted from Dicimus grates tibi by
    Paul Eber c. 1554
Translation by J.C. Jacobi

Melody from French Psalter 1551

Hymn by Johann Franck 1649
Translation by Catherine Winkworth

Melody by Johann Crüger 1649

Herr, ich ha- be miss- ge- han- delt, ja mich
ich bin nicht den Weg ge- wan- delt, den du
Lord to Thee I make con- fes- sion, I have
I have mul- ti- plied trans- gres- sion, Cho- sen

drückt der Sün- den Last; und itzt wollt' ich gern aus Schre-
mir ge- zei- get hast; und itzt wollt' ich gern aus Schre-
sinn'd and gone a- stray; Forced at last to see my er-
for my- self the way: Forced at last to see my er-

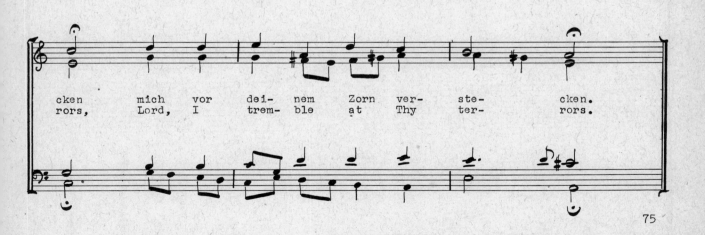

cken, mich vor dei- nem Zorn ver- ste- cken.
rors, Lord, I trem- ble at Thy ter- rors.

Cantata 48 Ich elender Mensch, wer wird mich erlösen (B.W. X p. 298)

Hymn from Schein's Cantional 1627   Melody from Dresden Gesangbuch 1593
Translation by Charles N. Boyd

Cantata 127 Herr Jesu Christ, wahr'r Mensch und Gott (B.W. XXVI p. 160)

Hymn by Paul Eber 1557   Melody of a French psalm adapted by Johann Doles 1785
Translation by Catherine Winkworth

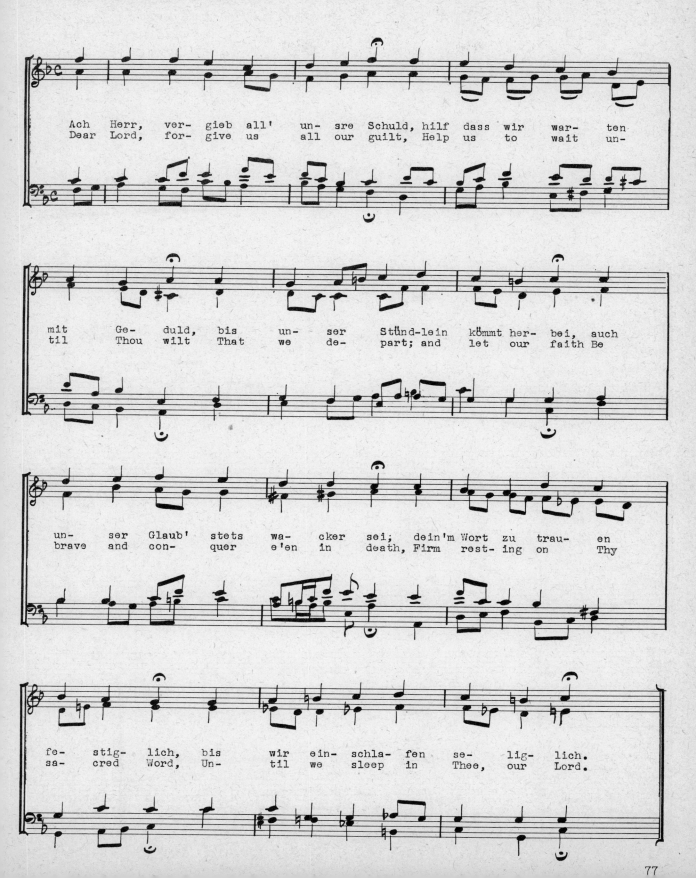

Ach Herr, ver-gieb all' un-sre Schuld, hilf dass wir war-ten
Dear Lord, for-give us all our guilt, Help us to wait un-

mit Ge-duld, bis un-ser Stünd-lein kömmt her-bei, auch
til Thou wilt That we de-part; and let our faith Be

un-ser Glaub' stets wa-cker sei; dein'm Wort zu trau-en
brave and con-quer e'en in death, Firm rest-ing on Thy

fe-stig-lich, bis wir ein-schla-fen se-lig-lich.
sa-cred Word, Un-til we sleep in Thee, our Lord.

Hymn by David Behme c. 1663   Melody from Gesangbuch der Böhmi'schen Brüder 1694
Translation by Catherine Winkworth

Herr, nun lass in Frie-   de,   le- bens- satt und
Lord, now let Thy serv-   ant   Pass in peace a-

mü-   de,   dei- nen Die- ner   fah-   ren
way;   I have had e-   nough of   life,

zu den Him- mels- schaa-   ren,   se- lig und im
Here I would not stay: Let me go if

Stil- len,   doch nach dei- nem Wil- len.
such Thy will,   With a heart at rest and still.

No. 69   HERZLICH LIEB HAB' ICH DICH, O HERR

St. John Passion (B.W. XII[1] p. 131)

Hymn by Martin Schalling 1567   Melody from Havs Kirchen Cantorei 1587
Translation by J. Troutbeck

79

+4151

se- hen dich in al- ler Freud', o Got- tes Sohn, mein
eyes shall see, O Son of God, Thy glo- rious face, My

Hei- land und Ge- na- den -thron! Herr Je- su Christ, er- hö- re mich, er-
Sav- iour and my Fount of Grace. Lord Je- sus Christ, O hear Thou me, O

hö- re mich, ich will dich prei- sen e- wig- lich!
hear Thou me, Thee will I praise e- ter- nal- ly.

x

80

Cantata 153 Schau lieber Gott wie meine Feind' (B.W. XXXII p. 46)

Hymn by Paul Gerhardt 1656   ·   Secular melody "Mein G'müt ist mir verwirrt" by
Translation by Henry Mills   Hans Leo Hassler 1601

Hymn by Paul Gerhardt 1656
Translation by Miss H.F.H. Johnston

Secular melody "Mein G'mũt ist mir verwirrt" by
Hans Leo Hassler 1601

Be- fiehl du dei- ne We- ge, und was dein Her- ze
der al- ler- treu- sten Pfle- ge des, wer den Him- mel
Com- mit thy ways to Je- sus, Thy bur- dens and thy
He from them all re-- leas- es, He all thy sor- row

krãnkt, Der Wol- ken, Luft und Win- den gibt
lenkt.
cares; Who gives the winds their cour- ses, And
shares.

We- ge, Lauf und Bahn, der wird auch We- ge
bounds the o- cean's shore, Will suf- fer not temp-

fin- den, die dein Fuss ge- hen kann.
ta- tion To rise be- yond Thy pow'r.

HERZLICH THUT MICH VERLANGEN
(B.W. XXXIX p. 185)

Hymn by Paul Gerhardt 1656   Secular melody "Mein G'müt ist mir verwirrt" by
Translation by Miss H.F.H. Johnston   Hans Leo Hassler 1601

Be- fiehl du dei- ne We- ge, und was dein Her- ze
der al- ler- treu-sten Pfle- ge des, der den Him- mel
Com- mit thy ways to Je- sus, Thy bur- dens and thy
He from them all re- leas- es, He all thy sor- row

kränkt, Der Wol- ken, Luft und Win- den gibt
lenkt.
cares; Who gives the winds their cour- ses, And
shares.

We- ge, Lauf und Bahn, der wird auch We- ge
bounds the o- cean's shore, Will suf- fer not temp-

fin- den, die dein Fuss ge- hen kann.
ta- tion To rise be- yond Thy pow'r.

St. Matthew Passion (B.W. IV p. 248)

Hymn by Paul Gerhardt 1656
Translation by Miss H.F.H. Johnston

Secular melody "Mein G'müt ist mir verwirrt" by
Hans Leo Hassler 1601

Hymn by Paul Gerhardt 1656
Translation by John S. Dwight

Secular melody "Mein G'müt ist mir verwirrt"
by Hans Leo Hassler 1601

O Haupt voll Blut und Wun-den, voll Schmerz und vol-ler
O Haupt, zu Spott ge-bun-den mit ei-ner Dor-nen-
O Head all bruis'd and woun-ded, Hung up to bru-tal
O Head, for shame sur-roun-ded With crown of cru-el

Hohn!   O Haupt, sonst schön ge-zie-ret mit
kron!   O Head, to hon-or won-ted, To
scorn!
thorn!

höchster Ehr' und Zier, jetzt a-ber hoch schim-
splendor all di-vine, Now out-rag'd and af-

pfi-ret: ge-grü-sset seist du mir.
fron-ted: All Hail, dear Mas-ter mine!

Hymn by Paul Gerhardt 1656
Translation by Miss H.F.H. Johnston

Secular melody "Mein G'müt ist mir verwirrt"
by Hans Leo Hassler 1601

St. Matthew Passion (B.W. IV, p. 51)

Hymn by Paul Gerhardt 1656
Translation by John S. Dwight

Secular melody "Mein G'müt ist mir verwirrt"
by Hans Leo Hassler 1601.

Hymn by Paul Gerhardt 1656
Translation by J. Troutbeck

Secular melody "Mein G'müt ist mir verwirrt"
by Hans Leo Hassler 1601

St. Matthew Passion (B.W. IV, p. 192)

Hymn by Johann Heermann 1630
Translation by John S. Dwight

Melody by Johann Crüger 1640

Wie   wun- der- bar- lich ist doch die- se   Stra- fe: der
What   won- drous pun- ish- ment is this to   ren- der!   For

gu-   er- ring Hir- te lei- det für die   Schaa- ten- fe;   die
err-   ing sheep is   slain the Shep- herd ten-   der;   The

Schuld be- zahlt der Her- re, der Ge-   rech- te,   für
Lord, the just one, for the ser- vant   pay- eth,   Who

sei-   ne Knech- te!
Him   be- tray- eth!

HERZLIEBSTER JESU, WAS HAST DU VERBROCHEN

St. John Passion (B.W. XII, p. 17)

Hymn by Johann Heermann 1630
Translation by J. Troutbeck

Melody by Johann Crüger 1640

No. 80   HILF, HERR JESU, LASS GELINGEN
              Christmas Oratorio (B.W. V², p. 166)

Hymn by Johann Rist 1642   Melody attributed to J.S. Bach 1734
Translation by J. Troutbeck

No. 81　　　　　ICH DANK' DIR, LIEBER HERRE

(B.W. XXXIX, p. 224)

Hymn by Johann Kolross　　　　　　　　Melody from Praxis pietatis 1662
Translation by C. Sanford Terry

Cantata 133 Ich freue mich in dir. (B.W. XXVIII, p. 80)

Hymn by Caspar Ziegler 1697   Melody from König's Harmonischer Liederschatz 1738
Translation by Elvera Wonderlich

Wohl- an! so will ich mich an dich o Je- su,
und soll- te gleich die Welt in tau- send Stü- cke
To Je- sus will I cling, From Him I'll wan- der
E'en should de-struc- tion rain Up- on this earth for-

hal- ten
spal- ten O Je- su! dir, nur dir, dir
nev- er, O Je- sus be my guide, And
ev- er.

leb' ich ganz al- lein; auf dich, al- lein auf
keep me by Thy side; A- lone in heav'n with

dich, o Je- su, schlaf' ich ein!
Thee Sweet slum- ber grant to me.

ICH HAB' MEIN SACH GOTT HEIMGESTELLT

(B.W. XXXIX, p. 226)

Hymn by Johannes Leon 1589
Translation by Catherine Winkworth

Melody from Rhau's Gesangbuch 1589

Ich hab' mein' Sach' Gott heim-ge- stellt, er mach's mit mir, wie's
My cause is God's, and I am still, Let Him do with me

ihm ge- fällt, soll ich all-hier noch län- ger leb'n, nicht
as He will; Wheth- er for me the race is run, Or

wi- der-streb'n, sei'm Will'n thu' ich mich ganz er- geb'n.
scarce be- gun, I ask no more His will be done!

IHR GESTIRN', IHR HOHLEN LÜFTE

(B.W. XXXIX, p. 236)

Hymn by Johann Franck 1655
Translation by Elvera Wonderlich

Melody by Christoph Peter 1655

Ihr Ge- stirn', ihr ho- hen Lüf- te,
tie- fes Rund, ihr dunk- len Klüf- te,
Stars a- bove in heav- en shin- ing,
Dark cliffs ris- ing, val- leys wind- ing,

und du, lich- tes Fir- ma- ment;
die der Wie- der- hall zer- trennt.
In the spa- cious fir- ma- ment;
Cav- erns wild with ech- oes rent,

Jauch- zet fröh- lich, lasst das Sin- gen,
Loud- ly let thy praise be ring- ing,

jetzt bis durch die Wol- ken dring- en.
Let thy song to heav- en be wing- ing.

IN DICH HAB' ICH GEHOFFET HERR

Christmas Oratorio (B.W. V², p. 190)

Hymn by Georg Weissel 1642
Translation by J. Troutbeck

Melody from Nürnberger Psalter 1581

IN DICH HAB' ICH GEHOFFET, HERR
St. Matthew Passion (B.W. IV, p. 151)

Hymn by Adam Reissner 1533
Translation by John S. Dwight

Melody from Nürnberger Psalter 1581

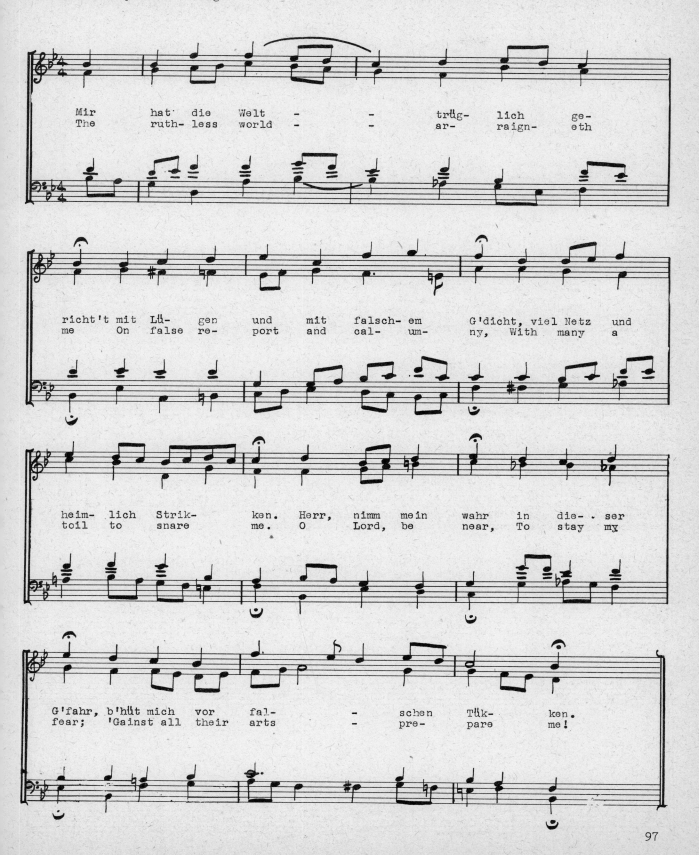

Mir hat die Welt — — trüg- lich ge-
The ruth- less world — — ar- raign- eth

richt't mit Lü- gen und mit falsch- em G'dicht, viel Netz und
me On false re- port and cal- um- ny, With many a

heim- lich Strik- ken. Herr, nimm mein wahr in die- ser
toil to snare me. O Lord, be near, To stay my

G'fahr, b'hüt mich vor fal- — schen Tük- ken.
fear; 'Gainst all their arts — pre- pare me!

Cantata 58 Ich bin ein guter Hirt (B.W. XX[1] p. 118)

Hymn by Christoph Homburg 1659   Melody from Hundert...Arien. Dresden, 1694
Translation by Charles N. Boyd

Ist   Gott   mein Schutz und   treu-   er   Hirt,   kein
With   God   my   guard   and   shep-   herd true,   Mis-

Un-   glück mich be-   rüh-   ren wird; weicht, al-   le   mei- ne
for-   tune   can- not   me   sub-due;   From   foes   He   will de-

Fein-   de,   die   ihr   mir   stif- tet   Angst und   Pein, es
liv-   er.   The   grief and   pain   they   plan   for   me   Up-

wird   zu eu- rem   Scha-   den sein; ich ha-   be   Gott zum
on   themselves shall turn-   ed be, For God   my   Friend is

Freun-   de, ich ha-   be   Gott zum   Freun-   de.
ev-   er, For   God   my   Friend is   ev-   er.

No. 88   JESU, DER DU MEINE SEELE

(B.W. XXXIX p. 228)

Hymn by Johann Rist 1641   Melody from Praxis Pietatis 1662
Translation by C. Sanford Terry

Je- su   der   du   mei-   ne   See-   le   hast durch
aus des   Teu-   fels   finst-   rer   Höh-   le   und der
Je- su,   Who de-   liv'-   rance   brought   me   By   Thine
In hell's chains had Sa-   tan   bound   me   If   Thou

deinen bittern Tod
schweren Sünden noth
own most bitter woe,
had'st not loved me so.

kräftiglich her-
From the tomb 'tis

ausgerissen und mich Solches lassen
Thou wilt call me, And in heaven wilt in-

wissen durch dein angenehmes Wort:
stall me. Through the strength Thy Word doth yield,

sei doch itzt, o Gott, mein Hort.
Be Thou still, dear Lord, my Shield!

JESU LEIDEN, PEIN UND TOD

St. John Passion (B.W. XII[1] p. 103)

Hymn by Paul Stockmann 1633
Translation by Dr. T.A. Lacey

Melody from Vulpius' Gesangbuch 1609

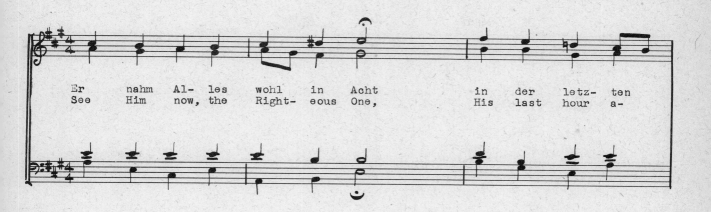

Er   nahm Al- les wohl in Acht   in der letz- ten
See   Him   now, the Right- eous One,   His last hour a-

Stun- de,   sei- ne Mut- ter   noch be- dacht',
bid- ing,   For His Mo- ther, faith- ful Son,

setzt ihr ein'n Vor-   mun-   de.   O Mensch, ma- che
Faith- ful care pro-   vid-   ing.   Work, O, man, for

Rich- tig- keit,   Gott und Mensch- en lie-   be,
right- eous- ness, God and man be- friend-   ing;

stirb da- rauf   ohn' al- les Leid, und dich nicht be-   trü -   be!
Death shall come with- out dis- tress, All dis- qui- et   end -   ing.

No. 90   JESU LEIDEN, PEIN UND TOD

St. John Passion (B.W. XII^{I}, p. 39)

Hymn by Paul Stockmann 1633   Melody from Vulpius' Gesangbuch 1609
Translation by Dr. T. A. Lacey

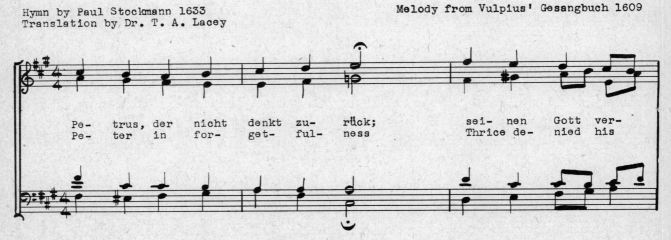

Pe- trus, der nicht denkt zu- rück;   sei- nen Gott ver-
Pe- ter in for- get- ful- ness   Thrice de- nied his

nei- net, der doch auf ein'n ern- sten Blick
Mas- ter; One look moved him to con- fess,

bit- ter- li- chen wei- net: Je- su, bli- cke
Weep-. ing, his dis- as- ter. Je- su, turn to

mich auch an, wenn ich nicht will bü- - ssen;
look on me, Who per- sist in sin- .- ning;

wenn ich Bö- ses hab' ge- than, rüh- re mein Ge- wis- sen.
Set my fet- tered con- science free, Free for new be- gin- ning.

Motette Jesu, meine Freude (B.W. XXXIX, p. 75)

Hymn by Johann Franck 1655   Melody by Johann Crüger 1653
Translation by Catherine Winkworth

JESU, MEINE FREUDE

Cantata 81 Jesus schläft, was soll ich hoffen? (B.W.XX[1] p. 24)

Hymn by Johann Franck 1655
Translation by Catherine Winkworth

Melody by Johann Crüger 1653

Un— ter dei— nen Schir— men bin ich vor den
Lass den Sa— tan wit— tern, lass den Feind er—
In Thine arm I rest me, Foes who would mo—
Though the earth be shak— ing, Ev'— ry heart be

Stür— men al— ler Fein— de frei
bit— tern, mir steht Je— sus bei.
lest me Can not reach me here;
quak— ing, Je— sus calms my fear;

Ob es jetzt gleich kracht und blitzt, ob— gleich Sünd und
Sin and hell in con— flict fell With their bit— ter

Höl— le schre— cken: Je— sus will mich de— cken.
storms as— sail me, Je— sus will not fail me.

JESU, MEINE FREUDE

(B.W. XXXIX, p. 231)

Hymn by Johann Franck 1655
Translation by Catherine Winkworth

Melody by Johann Crüger 1653

JESU, MEINE FREUDE

Motet Jesu, meine Freude (B.W. XXXIX, p. 61-84)

Hymn by Johann Franck 1655
Translation by Catherine Winkworth

Melody by Johann Crüger 1653

Je- su, mei- ne Freu- de, mei- nes Her- zens
ach, wie lang', ach lan- ge ist dem Her- zen
Je- su price- less trea- sure, Source of pur- est
Ah! how long I've pant- ed, And my heart hath

Wei- de, Je- su, mei- ne Zier,
ban- ge, und ver- langt nach dir!
plea- sure Tru- est Friend to me;
faint- ed, Thirst- ing Lord, for Thee!

Got- tes Lamm, mein Bräu- ti- gam, aus- ser dir soll
Thine I am, O spot- less lamb, I will suf- fer

mir auf Er- den nichts sonst Lie- bers wer- den.
nought to hide Thee, Nought I ask be- side Thee.

Cantata 190 Singet dem Herrn ein neues Lied. (B.W. XXXVII, p. 257)

Hymn by Johann Hermann c. 1591　　　　　　　　Melody from Wittenberg Cantilenae 15 91
Translation by C. Sanford Terry

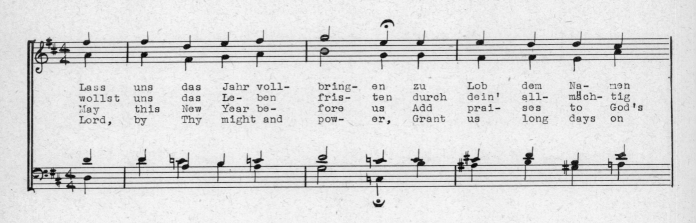

Lass　　uns　　das　　Jahr voll-　bring-　en　　zu　　Lob　　dem　　Na-　men
wollst　uns　　das　　Le-　ben　　fris-　ten　　durch　dein'　all-　mäch-　tig
May　　this　　New　Year be-　fore　us　　Add　　prai-　ses　　to　　God's
Lord,　by　　Thy　　might and　pow-　er,　　Grant　us　　long　days　on

dein,　　　　dass　　wir dem-　sel-　ben　　sin-　　　　gen　　in
Hand,　　er-　　halt' dein　lie-　be　　Chri-　　　　sten　und
name!　　　Good　　Christ-ians　all, in　　chor-　　　　us　　Your
earth;　　Thy　　rich-est　bless-ing　show-　　　　er　　On

der　Chris-　ten-　ge-　　mein;　　Dein'n　Se-　gen　zu　uns　wen-　de,
un-　ser　　Va-　ter-　land.　　　gieb　　Fried' an　al-　lem　En-　de;
loud-　est　car-　ols　frame!　　O　　shield us　neath Thy　strong wing!
our　dear　land of　birth!　　May　　this New　Year firm　peace bring!

108

gieb un-ver-fälscht im Lan- de dein se- lig-ma-chend Wort.
Die Heuchler mach' zu Schan- de hier und am al- lem Ort,
Stab-lish a- mong be- liev- ers Thine own Al- migh-ty realm,
And all earth's vain de- ceiv- ers Right ut- ter- ly o'er- whelm!

die Heuch-ler mach' zu Schan- de hier und am al- len Ort.
And all earth's vain de- ceiv- ers Right ut- ter- ly o'er- whelm.

No. .96   JESUS CHRISTUS, UNSER HEILAND

(B.W. XXXIX, p. 234)

Hymn by Martin Luther 1524   Melody from Erfurt Enchiridion 1524
Translation by C.S. Terry

Je- sus Chri- - stus, un- ser Hei- land,
Christ our Sav- - iour hath re- deemed us,

der von uns den Got- tes er zorn - - wand,
Turned His Fa- ther's an- ger from - - us,

durch das bitt- re Lei - - den sein half
By the bit- ter cross He bore, And

er uns aus der Höl- - - len- tan's pein.
saved us all from Sa- - - tan's power.

JESUS, MEINE ZUVERSICHT

(B.W. XXXIX,.p. 235)

Hymn by Luise Henriette of Brandenburg 1653   Melody from Crügers Praxis Pietatis 1653
Translation by Catherine Winkworth

Je-   sus, mei- ne   Zu-   ver- sicht   und   mein Hei- land,
Die- ses weiss ich, soll ich nicht   da-   rum mich zu-
Je-   sus Christ, my sure de- fence   And   my Sav- iour
Know- ing this my   con- fi- dence   Rests   up- on   the

ist   im   Le-   ben:
frie- den ge-   ben?   Was   die   lan-   ge
ev-   er   liv-   eth;
hope it   giv-   eth,   Though the   night of

To-   des- nacht   mir   auch für Ge-   dan-   ken macht.
death be   fraught   Still with many an   anx-   ious thought.

No. 98   JESUS, MEINE ZUVERSICHT

Cantata 145 So du mit deinem Munde bekennest Jesum (B.W. XXX, p. 95)

Hymn by Caspar Neumann c. 1700   Melody from Crüger's Praxis Pietatis 1653
Translation by C. Sanford Terry

Auf, mein Herz! Des Her- ren Tag   hat die Nacht der
Chri- stus, der im Gra- be lag,   ist im To- de
Up, my soul, 'tis God's great day,   Death no long- er
He Who in the dark grave lay   Ris'n and glo- rious

Furcht ver- trie- ben: Nun- mehr bin ich   recht ge- tröst't,
nicht ge- blie- ben.
can en- thral us!   Ev- er will I   trust in Him
goes be- fore us.

Je- sus hat die Welt er- löst.
Who hath brought the world from sin.

(B.W. XXXIX, p. 238)

Hymn by Martin Luther 1524   Melody from Klug's Geistliche Lieder 1535
Translation by Dr. Bacon

Komm,   Gott   Schö-   pfer, hei-   li-   ger   Geist, be-
Come,   God   Cre-   a-   tor,   Ho-   ly   Ghost, And

such' das Herz der   Men-schen dein, mit   Gna-   den sie füll'
vis-it thou these   souls of men; Fill them with gra-ces,

wie   du   weisst, dass   dein   Ge-schöpf soll   für   dir   sein.
as   thou dost, Thy   cre-   tures make   pure a-   gain.

113

Cantata 108 Es ist euch gut, dass ich hingehe (B.W. XXIII, p. 230)

Hymn by Paul Gerhardt 1653   Melody from Schumann's Geistliche Lieder 1539
Translation by C. Sanford Terry

Dein Geist, den Gott vom Him- mel giebt, der lei- tet Al- les,
His Spir- it, Whom God sends at need, Us on His right-eous

was ihn liebt, auf wohl ge- bahn- ten We- gen. Er setzt und
paths will lead, Our foot- steps e'er pro- tect- ing. They shall not

rich- tet un- sern Fuss, dass er nicht an- ders tre- ten
wan- der from His ways, Nor be en- snared in Sa- tan's

muss, als wo man find't den Se- gen.
maze, Who fol- low His di- rect- ing.

Hymn by Tobias Clausnitzer 1663   Melody from Ahle's Sonntagsandachten 1664
Translation by Catherine Winkworth

Lieb- ster Je- su   wir sind hier,   dich und dein Wort
len- ke Sin- nen   und Be- gier   auf die süssen
Bles- sed Je- su,   at   Thy word   We   are gath-ered
Let our hearts and souls be stirred   Now to   seek and

an- zu- hö-   ren;   dass die Her- zen
Him- mels- leh-   ren,   dass die Her- zen
all to   hear   Thee;   By   Thy teach- ings
love and fear   Thee,   By   Thy teach- ings

von der Er- den   ganz zu dir ge-   zo- gen wer-   den.
sweet and ho- ly   Drawn from earth to love Thee sole- ly.

LOBT GOTT, IHR CHRISTEN, ALLZUGLEICH

(B.W. XXXIX, p. 241)

Hymn by Nicolaus Herman c. 1554
Translation by August Crill

Melody by Nicolaus Herman 1554

Lobt Gott, ihr Chri- sten all- zu- gleich, in sei- nem höch- sten
Praise God, the Lord, ye songs of men, Be- fore His high- est

Thron; der heut' auf- schleusst sein Him- mel- reich und
Throne, To- day He o- pens heav'n a- gain, And

schenkt uns sei- nen Sohn, – und schenkt uns sei- nen Sohn.
gives us His Own Son, – And gives us His Own Son.

MACH'S MIT MIR, GOTT, NACH DEINER GÜT'

(B.W. XXXIX, p. 242)

Hymn by Johann Schein 1628
Translation by Catherine Winkworth

Melody by Johann Schein 1628

Mach's mit mir, Gott, nach dei- ner Güt', hilf
was ich dich bitt', ver- sag' mir nicht, wenn
Deal with me, God, in mer- cy now, Oh
Thine ear to me in pi- ty bow; When

mir in mei- nem Lei- den, so nimm sie, Herr, in
mei- ne Seel' will schei- den; Re- ceive her, as her
help me in my utter woe
hence my soul must quickly go,

dei- ne Hand', ist Al- les gut, wenn gut das End'.
God and Friend, For all is right if right the end.

Cantata 10 Meine Seel' erhebt den Herren (B.W. I, p. 303)

Hymn by Gloria Patri   Melody Tonus peregrinus
Translation anonymous

Lob und Preis sei Gott dem Va- ter   und dem
Glo- ry be to God the Fa- ther   and the

Sohn   und   dem hei- li- gen Gei-
Son,   and   to the Ho- ly Ghost

ste,   wie es   war im An- fang jetzt und
-    As it was in the be- gin-

im- mer dar   und von E- wig- keit zu
ning is now   and shall be ev- er-

E— more. wig- keit, A— men.
A— men.

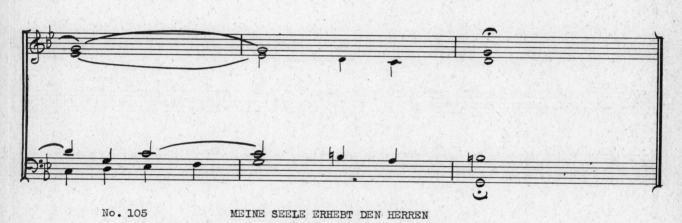

No. 105　　　　MEINE SEELE ERHEBT DEN HERREN

(B.W. XXXIX, p. 212)

Hymn Benediction　　　　　　　　　　　　Melody Tonus peregrinus
Translation anonymous

Gott — sei uns gnä- dig und barm-
The — Lord for ev- er bless and

her-   zig   und -
keep   us,   and

geb' uns sei- nen gött-   li-   chen   Se-   -
ev- er- more give us   His   bless-   -

gen.
ing.

Cantata 70 Wachet betet seid bereit (B.W. XVI, p. 368)

Hymn by Christian Keimann 1658   Melody from Hammerschmiedt's Fest, Bus und
Translation by C. Sanford Terry   Danck Lieder 1658

Nicht nach Welt, nach Himmel nicht   meine Seele
Heav'n nor earth are my delight,   Other bourne my

wünscht und sehnet,   Jesum wünsch' ich und sein Licht, der mich
soul inviteth.   Jesus is my Hope, my Light, God and

hat mit Gott versöhnet,   der mich frei macht
man He reconcileth,   He hath borne my

vom Gericht,   meinen Jesum lass' ich nicht.
load of sin,   Never will I part from Him.

* Chord third appears in instrumental accompaniment.

121

MIT FRIED' UND FREUD' ICH FAHR DAHIN

(B.W. XXXIX, p. 245)

Hymn by Martin Luther 1524
Translation by Catherine Winkworth

Melody from Walter's Geystliche gesangk
Buchleyn 1524

Mit Fried' und Freud' ich fahr' da-hin in Got-tes Wil-
In peace and joy I now de-part, Ac-cord-ing to God's

le, ge-trost ist mir mein Herz und Sinn, sanft-
will, For full of com-fort is my heart, So

-calm and still-le. Wie Gott mir vor hei-ssen
calm and sweet and still; So doth God His pro-mise

hat, der Tod ist mein Schlaf wor-den.
keep, And death to me is but a sleep.

Cantata 83 Erfreute Zeit im neuen Bunde (B.W. XX^1, p. 76)

Hymn by Martin Luther 1524
Translation by Catherine Winkworth

Melody from Walter's Geystliche gesangk Buchleyn 1524

Er ist das Heil und se-lig Licht für - die Hei-
He is the hea-then's sa-ving light, And He will gent-ly

den, zu er-leuch-ten, die dich ken - - nen
lead Those who now know Thee not - - a-

nicht, und zu wei- den. Er ist dein's Volks
right And in His pastures feed: While His peo- ples'

I-sra-el der Preis, Ehr, Freud' und Won- ne.
joy He is, Their Sun, their Glo- ry, and their bliss.

(B.W. XXXIX, p. 247)

Hymn by Paul Gerhardt 1648   Melody attributed to J.S. Bach 1736
Translation by Mrs. Eric Findlater

Nicht   so   trau- rig, nicht so   sehr,   mei- ne
dass   dir   Gott   Glück, Gut und   Ehr'   nicht so
Ah! grieve not so,   nor so la- ment, My -
Be- cause some joys to oth- ers sent Thy -

See- le, sei be-   trübt,
viel, wie An- dern   gibt;   nimm für-   lieb mit dei- nem
soul! nor trou- bled sigh,   Take all   as   love that seems se-
Fa- ther may de-   ny;

Gott;   hast du Gott, so hat's nicht   Noth.
vere There is no want if God   is   near.

Cantata 197 Gott ist uns're Zuversicht (B.W. XIII[1], p. 128)

Hymn by Martin Luther 1524   Melody from Walter's Geystliche gesangk Buchleyn 1524
Translation by A.T. Russell

Du sü- sse Lieb', schenk' - uns dei- ne Gunst, lass
Spir- it of love, now - our spir-its bless; Them

uns em- pfin - den der Lie- be Brunst, dass wir
with thy own - heaven-ly fire pos- sess; That in

uns von Her- zen ein an- der lie- ben,
heart u- nit- ing, In peace de- light- ing,

und in Fried' auf ei - nem Sin - ne blei - ben.
We may hence-forth all be one in spir - it.

Ky- ri- e mer - e- leis!
Have mer - cy, Lord.

No. 111　　　　　　NUN DANKET ALLE GOTT

(B.W. XXXIX, p. 248)

Hymn by Martin Rinkart 1648　　　　　　　　Melody by Johann Crüger 1648
Translation by Catherine Winkworth

Nun　dan-ket al- le Gott　　mit Her- zen, Mund und
der　gros- se Din- ge thut　　an uns und al- len
Now　thank we all our God,　With heart and hands and
Who　won-drous things hath done,　In whom His world re-

Hän-
En-
den,
voi-   ces;

der
Who
uns
from
von
our
Mut-   ter-
mo-   thers'
leib
arms
und
Hath

Kin-   des-,
bless'd
bei-   nen
u   on
an
our
way

un-
With
zäh-   lig
count- less
viel zu
gifts of

gut
love,
und
And
noch jetz
still is
und
ours
ge-   than.
to-   day.

NUN DANKET ALLE GOTT

Trauungschoral (B.W. XIII[1], p. 149)

Hymn by Martin Rinkart 1648
Translation by Catherine Winkworth

Melody by Johann Crüger 1648

Nun dan- ket al- le Gott   mit   Her- zen, Mund und
der gros- se Din- ge thut   an   uns und al- len
Now thank we all our God,   With   heart and hands and
Who won- drous things hath done, In   whom His world re-

Hän-   den,
En-   den;   der   uns von Mut- ter leib   und
voi-   ces,
joi-   ces;   Who   from our mo- thers' arms   Hath

Kin- des- bei- nen   an un- zäh- lig viel zu
bless'd us on our   way With count- less gifts of

gut   und noch jetz und ge- than.
love,   And still is ours to- day.

NUN FREUT EUCH, GOTTES KINDER ALL'

(B.W. XXXIX p. 248)

Hymn by Erasmus Alber c. 1549
Translation by Elvera Wonderlich

Melody from a broadsheet c. 1546

Nun freut euch, Got- tes Kin- der all, der all, der
O chil- dren of your God, re- joice, To

Herr fährt auf mit gro- ssem Schall, lob- sin- get ihm lob-
Him lift up both heart and voice. Praise ye the Lord, praise

sin- get ihm, lob- sin- get ihm mit hel- ler Stimm'!
ye the Lord, Sing praise to Him with one ac- cord.

Cantata 36 Schwingt freudig euch empor (B.W. VII, p. 258)

Hymn by Martin Luther 1524
Translation by Richard Massie

Melody from Erfurt Enchiridion 1524

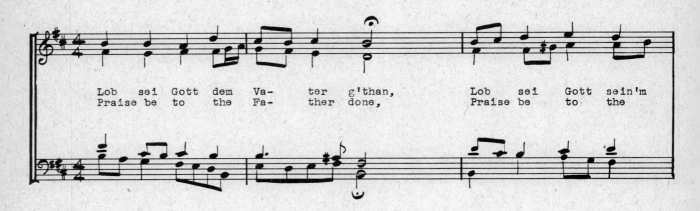

Lob sei Gott dem Va- ter g'than,   Lob sei Gott sein'm
Praise be to the Fa- ther done,   Praise be to the

ein'- gen Sohn,   Lob sei Gott dem   heil'- gen Geist
on- ly Son,   Prai- ses to the   Spir- it be,

im- mer und in E- wig- keit.
Now and to e- ter- ni- ty.

Hymn by Paul Gerhardt 1647
Translation by H.J. Buckoll

Melody by Nikolaus Selnecker 1587

Sprich Ja zu meinen Thaschütten, hilf
selbst das Beste ranen then; den
An- fang, Mitt'l und Ende, ach
Herr, zum Besten wende.

Mit Segen mich bedeite Hütte, mein
Herz sei dein thought ne directe, dein
Wort sei mein gin- ne Speinging, bis
ich zum Himmel reite se.

Thou all I do protectting, And
ev'ry Thy thought dispossing? First,
last, Be- food be giv- en, Let
all to Good soar to heav- en!

Lord, pour Thy spirit's blessing, This
heart Thy home possessing, Thy
Word my food be given, Till
hence I soar to heaven!

131

Hymn by Johann Graumann 1540
Translation by Catherine Winkworth

Melody by Johann Kugelmann 1540

Gras vom Re— che, ein' Blum' und
as the flow— ers, And ev— en

fal— lend Laub der Wind nur drü— ber
so we fade. A storm wind o'er them

we— het, so ist es nim— mer
pass— es, And all their bloom is

da; al— so der Mensch ver— ge—
o'er; We wi— ther like the grass—

het,   sein End',   das   ist -   ihm   nah.
es,   Our   place knows   us   no   more.

No. 117   NUN SICH DER TAG GEENDET HAT

                           (B.W. XXXIX, p. 252)

Hymn by Johann Hertzog 1670   Melody from Krieger's Neue Arien 1667
Translation by Catherine Winkworth

Nun   sich der Tag ge- en- det hat, und   kei- ne Sonn' mehr scheint, schläft
Now   that the sun doth shine no more, And   day hath reach'd its close, They

Al- les, was sich ab- ge- matt', und   was   zu- vor   ge- weint.
calm-ly   sleep who   wept be-fore, The   wea- ried find   re- pose.

134

Cantata 20 O Ewigkeit, du Donnerwort (B.W. II, p. 327)

Hymn by Johann Rist 1642
Translation by J.C. Jacobi

Melody from Crügers Praxis pietatis 1653

O   E- wig- keit, du   Don- ner- wort, o   Home-
E- ter- ni- ty, tre- men- dous word, o   Home-

Schwert, das durch die See- le bohrt, o   An- fang son- der
strik- ing point, heart- pierc- ing sword, Be- gin- ning with- out

En- de   Nimm du mich, wenn es dir ge- fällt, Herr
end- ing!   Lord Je- su, when it pleas- es Thee, Bring

Je- su, in dein Freu- den- zelt.
me to blest e- ter- ni- ty.

O GOTT, DU FROMMER GOTT

Cantata 45 Es ist dir gesagt, Mensch, was gut ist (B.W. X p. 186)

Hymn by Johann Heermann 1630
Translation by Catherine Winkworth

Melody from Fritsch's Himmels-Lust und
Welt-Unlust 1679

Gieb, dass ich thu' mit Fleiss, was mir zu thun ge-
And grant me, Lord, to do, With read-y heart and

büh- ret, wo- zu mich dein Be- fehl in
will- ing, What- e'er Thou shalt com- mand, My

mei- nem Stan- de füh- ret. Gieb, dass ich's thu e
call- ing here ful- fill- ing, And do it when I

bald, Zu der Zeit, da ich soll; und
ought, With all my strength; and bless the

wenn ich's thu', so gieb, dass es ge- ra- the wohl.
work I thus have wrought, For Thou must give suc- cess.

No. 120   O GOTT, DU FROMMER GOTT

Cantata 24 Ein ungefärbt Gemüthe (B.W. VI, p. 150)

Hymn by Johann Heermann 1630   Melody from Meiningishes Gesangbuch 1693
Translation by Catherine Winkworth

O Gott, du from- mer Gott, du Brunn- quell
O God, Thou faith- ful God, Thou Foun- tain

137

aller Ga-ben, ohn' den nichts ist, was ist, von
al-ev-er flow-ing, With-out whom no-thing is, All

dem wir Al-les ha-ben: ge-sun-den Leib gieb
per-fect All gifts be-stow-ing; A pure and heal-thy

mir, und dass in sol-chem Leib ein' un-ver-letz-te
frame O give me, and with-in A con-science free from

Seel' und rein Ge-wis-sen bleib!
blame, A soul un-hurt by sin.

Cantata 46 Schauet doch und sehet, ob irgend ein Schmerz sei (B.W. X, p. 236)

Hymn by Balthasar Schnurr 1632   Melody attributed to Melchior Franck 1632
Translation by C. Sanford Terry

O   gro-sser Gott der   Treu', weil   vor   dir   Nie- mand gilt als
O   Lord, Thou God of   Truth, Be-   fore Whom none may   stand If

dein Sohn Je- sus   Christ,   der   dei- nen Zorn ge-
Je-   sus   Christ Thy   Son   Stay   not   Thy wrath- ful

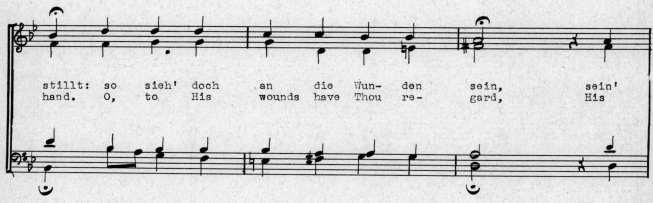

stillt: so sieh' doch   an   die Wun- den   sein,   sein'
hand. O,   to   His   wounds have Thou re-   gard,   His

Mar- ter, Angst und schwe- re Pein. Um sei- net- wil- len
an- guish, pain, and bo- dy marred: For His dear sake, O

scho- ne, und nicht nach Sün- den loh- ne!
spare us, And on Thy mer- cy bear us!

No. 122   O HERRE GOTT, DEIN GÖTTLICH WORT

Cantata 184 Erwünschtes Freudenlicht (B.W. XXXVII, p. 95)

Hymn from Erfurt Enchiridion 1527   Melody from Erfurt Enchiridion 1527
Translation from Moravian Hymn Book 1754

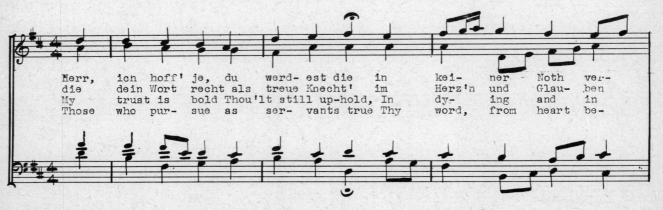

Herr, ich hoff' je, du werd- est die in kei- ner Noth ver-
die dein Wort recht als treue Knecht' im Herz'n und Glau- ben
My trust is bold Thou'lt still up-hold, In dy- ing and in
Those who pur- sue as ser- vants true Thy word, from heart be-

las- - - sen, giebst ihn'n be- reit die
fas- - - sen;
liv- - - ing Great bliss ev'n now Thou
liev- - - ing.

Se- lig- keit und läss'st sie nicht ver- der- ben. O
dost be- stow On them: they ne'er shall per- ish. O

Herr durch dich bitt' ich, lass mich fröh- lich und se- lig
Lord, let me be kept through Thee, In all my course me

ster- - - ben.
cher- - - ish.

141

O TRAURIGKEIT, O HERZELEID

(B.W. XXXIX, p. 257)

Hymn by Johann Rist 1641
Translation by Catherine Winkworth

Melody from Rist's Himlischer Lieder 1641

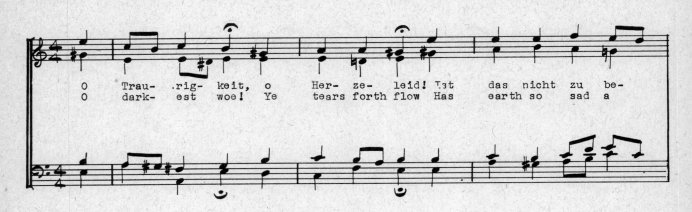

O Trau- .rig- keit, o Her- ze- leid! Ist das nicht zu be-
O dark- est woe! Ye tears forth flow Has earth so sad a

kla- gen?   Got- tes Va- ters ei- nigs Kind
won- der,   That the fa- ther's on- ly Son

wird zu Grab ge- tra- gen.
Now lies bu- ried yon- der!

No. 124   O WELT, ICH MUSS DICH LASSEN

(B.W. XXXIX, p. 251)

Hymn by Paul Gerhardt 1648
Translation by Catherine Winkworth

Melody by Heinrich Isaac c. 1510

O   Welt, sieh' hier dein Le-   ben   am   Stamm des   Kreu- zes
Oh,   world! be-hold up-   on the tree Thy   Life   is   hang- ing

schwe- ben,   dein **Heil sinkt** in   den   Tod,   der
now for thee, Thy   Sav- iour yields His dying breath;   The

gros- se **Fürst** der   Eh- ren   lässt   wil- lig sich be-
might- y   **Prince** of   glory now   For   thee doth un- re-

schwe- ren   mit   Schlä- ten, Hohn und   gros- sem   Spott.
sisting bow To.. cru- el stripes, To   scorn and   death.

143

O WELT ICH MUSS DICH LASSEN

.St. Matthew Passion.(B.W. IV, p. 164)

Hymn by Paul Gerhardt 1648
Translation by J. Troutbeck

Melody by Heinrich Isaac c. 1510

Wer hat dich so ge-schla- gen, mein Heil, und dich mit
O Lord, who dares to smite Thee, And false-ly to in-

Pla- gen so ü- bel zu- ge- richt? Du
dict Thee, De- ride and mock Thee so? Thou

bist ja nicht ein Sün- der, wie wir und un- sre
canst not need con- fes- sion, Who know- est not trans-

Kin- der; von Mis- se- tha- ten weisst du nicht.
gres- sion, As we and all our chil- dren know.

O WELT, ICH MUSS DICH LASSEN

St. John Passion (B.W. XII¹, p. 31)

Hymn by Paul Gerhardt 1648
Translation by J. Troutbeck

Melody by Heinrich Isaac c. 1510

Wer hat dich so ge- schla- gen, mein Heil, und dich mit
O Lord, who dares to smite Thee? And false-ly to in-

Pla- gen so ü- bel zu ge- rich't? Du
dite Thee, De- ride and mock Thee so? Thou

bist ja nicht ein Sün- der, wie wir und un- sre
need- est not con- fes- sion, Who know- est not trans-

Kin- der, von Mis- se- tha- ten weisst du nicht.
gres- sion, As we and all our chil- dren know.

(B.W. XXXIX, p. 258)

Hymn by Simon Dach 1635   Melody from Gesangbuch der Böhmischen Brüder 1566
Translation by Catherine Winkworth

O wie se-lig seid ihr doch, ihr From-men,
Oh how blest are ye be-yond our tell-ing

die ihr durch den Tod zu Gott ge-kom-men! Ihr
Who have pass'd through death, with God are dwell-ing, For

seid ent-gan-gen al-ler Noth, die uns noch
ev-er ris-en From the trou-bles of our

hält ge-fan-gen.
earth-ly pri-son.

Cantata 65 Sie werden aus Saba Alle kommen (B.W. XVI, p. 152)

Hymn adapted from 14th century Latin hymn
Translation by H.M. MacGill

Melody from Lossius' Psalmodia 1553

Die Kön'-ge aus Sa-ba ka - men dar,
And king-ly pil-grims, long fore-told,

ka - - - men dar, Gold, Weih-rauch
Al - le - lu - ja. From east bring

Myrr-hen brach-ten sie dar, Al - le - lu-
in-cense, myrrh, and gold. Al - le - lu-

ja, Al-le - - - lu- ja!
ja, Al-le - - - lu- ja!

Cantata 180 Schmücke dich, o liebe Seele (B.W. XXXV, p. 322)

Hymn by Johann Franck 1649   Melody by Johann Crüger 1649
Translation by Catherine Winkworth

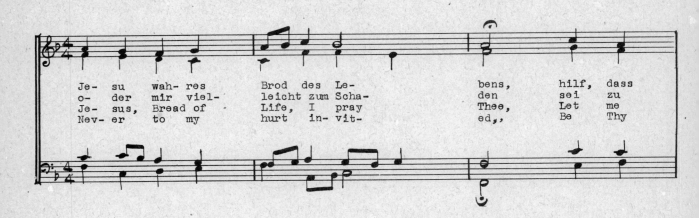

Je- su   wah- res   Brod des Le-   bens,   hilf, dass
o-   der   mir viel-   leicht zum Scha-   den   sei zu
Je- sus, Bread of   Life, I pray   ed,,   Let me
Nev- er   to my   hurt in-vit-   ed,,   Be Thy

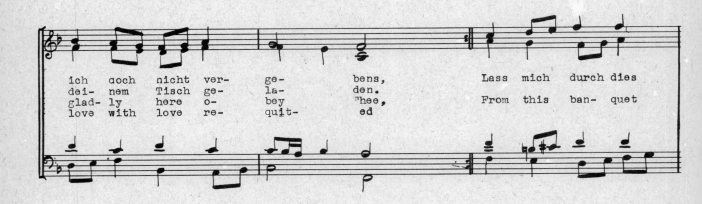

ich ooch nicht ver-   ge-   bens,   Lass mich durch dies
dei- nem   Tisch ge-   la-   den.   From this ban- quet
glad-ly   here o-   bey   Thee,
love with love re-   quit-   ed

See- len- Es-mea-   sen   dei- ne   Lie- be recht er-
let me   mea-   sure,   Lord how   vast and deep its

mes - sen, dass ich auch, wie jetzt auf Er - en,
trea - sure; Through the gifts Thou here dost give me

mög ein Gast im Him - mel wer - den.
As Thy guest in heav - en re - ceive me.

No. 130   SCHWING' DICH AUF ZU DEINEM GOTT

Cantata 40 Dazu ist erschienen der Sohn Gottes (B.W. VII, p. 327)

Hymn by Paul Gerhardt 1653   Melody revised by J.S. Bach 1769
Translation by Albert Riemenschneider

Schüt-tle dei - nen Kopf und sprich: fleuch, du al - te
Lift thy head and proud-ly sing: Flee, de - spis - ed

No. 131   SINGEN WIR AUS HERZENS GRUND

Cantata 187 Es wartet Alles auf dich (B.W. XXXVII, p. 191)

Hymn anonymous 16th century   Melody from Gesangbuch der Brüder inn Behemen und
Translation by C. Sanford Terry   Merherrn, 1544

Gott hat die Erd' schön zu- ge- richt't,
Wir dan- ken sehr und bit- ten ihn,
Well hath our God the world or- dained!
Now thank we Him and praise Him too

lässt's an Nah- rung man- geln nicht;
dass er uns geb! des Gei- stes Sinn,
Good things on us He hath raihed;
Who doth our dull sense re- new,

Berg und Thal, die macht er nass,
dass wir sol- ches recht ver- steh'n,
His the val- leys and the hills,
Mak- eth us to grow in grace

dass dem Vieh auch wächst sein Gras;
stets nach sein'n Ge- bo- ten geh'n,
Herbs and pas- ture- feed- ing rills,
And t'ward His law set our face.

151

aus   der   Er — den   Wein   und   Brod
sei-   nen   Na-   men   ma-   chen   gross
His   the   au-   tumn's   har-   vest   sheaves.
His   name   come   now,   glo-   ri-   fy,

schaf-   fet   Gott,   und   giebt's   uns   satt,
in   Chri-   sto   ohn'   ty   Un-   fair   ter-   lass:
Earth   with   plen-   ty   fair   He   wréathes,
Sing   with   joy   and   mel-   o-   dy,

dass   der   Mensch   sein   Le-   ben   hat.
so   sing'n   wir   das   Gra-   ti-   as.
Life   in-   to   our   be-   ing   breathes.
Gra-   ti-   as   to   God   on   high!

Cantata 115 Mache dich, mein Geist, bereit (B.W. XXIV, p. 132)

Hymn by Johann Freystein 1697   Melody from Hundert ahnmutig und sonderbar geistlicher
Translation by C.S. Terry   Arien 1694

No. 133   VALET WILL ICH DIR GEBEN
                      (B.W. XXXIX p. 263)

Hymn by Valerius Herberger 1614   Melody by Melchior Teschner 1613
Translation by Catherine Winkworth

Va-   let will ich   dir   ge-   ben, du   ar- ge   fa- sche
dein sünd-lich bö-   ses   Le-   ben   durch aus mir nicht ge-
Fare- well I   glad- ly   bid   Thee, False e-   vil world fare-
Thy   life is   dark and   sin-   ful, With thee I   would not

Welt,   Im   Him- mel ist   gut woh-   nen, hin-
fällt.   In   heav'n are joys un- troub-   led, I
well!   In
dwell:

auf steht mein Be- gier,   da   wird Gott e-   wig
long for   that bright sphere   Where God re- wards them
               Be-bright

loh-   nen dem, der — ihm dient all-   hier.
dou-   bled Who serv'd Him tru- ly   here.

 # The bass is A in the Bach Gesellschaft Edition

154

VALET WILL ICH DIR GEBEN

St. John Passion (B.W. XII^I, p. 95)

Hymn by Valerius Herberger 1614
Translation by J. Troutbeck

Melody by Melchior Teschner 1613

No. 135   VATER UNSER IM HIMMELREICH

Cantata 90 Es reifet euch ein schrecklich Ende (B.W. XX^1, p. 214)

Hymn translated from Latin by Martin Moller 1584   Melody from Schumann's
Translation by Elvera Wonderlich   Geistliche Lieder 1539

Leit' uns mit dei- ner rech- ten Hand; und seg- ne un- ser'
Oh guide us Lord with Thy right hand, And bless and save our

Stadt und Land: gieb uns all- zeit dein heil- ges Wort, be-
fa- ther- land: Pro- tect us with Thy Ho- ly Word, From

hüt' vor Teu- fel's List und Mord, ver- leih' ein sel'- ges
Sa- tan's lure re- move us, Lord, And grant us ho- ly

Stün- de- lein, auf dass wir e- wig bei dir sein!
peace at last With Thee in heav'n when life is past.

156

VATER UNSER IM HIMMELREICH
St. John Passion B.W. XII (Preface p. 16)

Hymn by Martin Luther 1539   Melody from Schumann's Geistliche Lieder 1539
Translation by J. Troutbeck

Dein Will' ge- scheh', Herr Gott zu- gleich auf Er- den wie im
Thy will, O Lord, our God, be done, On earth, as round Thy

Him- mel- reich; gieb uns Ge- duld in Lei- dens- zeit, Ge-
heav'n-ly throne. In time of sor- row pa- tience give, O-

hor- sam sein in Lieb' und Leid, wehr' und steur! al- lem
be- dient ev- er make us live. With Thy re- strain-ing

Fleisch und Blut, das wi- der dei- nen Wil- len thut.
Spir- it fill Each heart that strives a- gainst Thy will.

VOM HIMMEL HOCH DA KOM ICH HER

Christmas Oratorio (B.W. v², p. 66)

Hymn by Paul Gerhardt 1667
Translation by J. Troutbeck

Melody from Schumann's Geistliche Lieder 1539

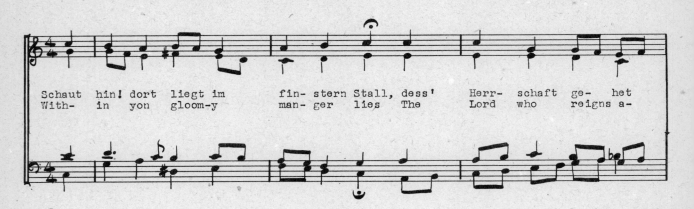

Schaut hin! dort liegt im fin- stern Stall, dess' Herr- schaft ge- het
With- in yon gloom- y man- ger lies The Lord who reigns a-

ü- ber- all. Da Spei- se vor- mals sucht' ein Rind, da
bove the skies. With- in the stall where beasts have fed The

ru- het jetzt der Jung- frau'n Kind.
Vir- gin born doth lay His head.

Cantata 73 Herr, wie du willst (B.W. XVIII, p. 104)

Hymn by Ludwig Helmbold 1563   Melody from Magdeburg's Christliche und
Translation by Catherine Winkworth   Tröstliche Tischgesenge 1571

Das ist des Va- ters Wil- le,   der   uns er- schaf- fen
For such His will who made   us,   The   Fa- ther seeks our

hat;   sein   Sohn hat Gut's die   Fül-   le   er-
good;   The   Son hath grace to   aid   us,   And

wor- ben uns aus Gnad';   auch   Gott, der heil'- ge
save us by His blood;   His   Spi- rit rules our

159

Geist, im Glau- ben uns re- gie- ret, zum

ways, By faith in us a- bid- ing, To

Reich des Him- mels füh- ret: ihm sei Lob, Ehr' und

heav'n our foot- steps guid- ing; To Him be thanks and

Preis.

praise.

No. 139   WACHET AUF RUFT UNS DIE STIMME

Cantata 140 Wachet auf, ruft uns die Stimme (B.W. XXVIII, p. 284)

Hymn by Philipp Nicolai 1599   Melody by Philipp Nicolai 1599
Translation by Catherine Winkworth

Glo-   ri-   a   sei   dir   ge-   sun
Von   zwölf   Per-   len   sind   die   Pfor-
Now   let   all   the   heavens a-   dore
Of   one   pearl   each   shin-   ing   por-

gen   mit   Men-   schen   und   eng-
ten   an   dei-   ner   Stadt; wir
Thee,   And   men   and   an-   gels
tal,   Where   we   are   with   the

li-   schen   Zun-   -   gen,   mit
sind   Con-   sor-   -   ten   der
sing   be-   fore   Thee,   With
choir   im-   mor-   tal   Of

Har-   fen   und   mit   Cym-   beln   schon.
En-   gel   hoch   um   dei-   nen   Thron.
harp   and   cym-   bal's   clear- est   tone;
an-   gels   round   Thy   dazz-   ling   throne;

Kein   Aug'   hat   je   ge-   spürt,
Nor   eye   hath   seen,   nor   ear

Kein   Ohr   hat   je   ge-   hört
Hath   yet   at-   tain'd   to   hear

sol-   che   Freu-   de.   Dess
What   there   is   ours,   But

sind   wir   froh,   i-   o!   i-   o!   e-
we   re-   joice, and   sing   to   Thee   Our

wig   in   dul- ci   ju-   bi-   lo.
hymn   of   joy e-   ter-   nal-   ly.

No. 140   WARUM BETRÜBST DU DICH, MEIN HERZ

Cantata 47 Wer sich selbst erhöhet (B.W. X, p. 274)

Hymn attributed to Hans Sachs c. 1560   Melody by Monoetius 1565
Translation by Catherine Winkworth

Der zeitlichen Ehr' will ich gern ent- behr'n, du   woll'st mir nur das
What here may shine I   all re- sign, If   the   e- ter- nal

Ew'ge ge- wahr'n, das   du er- wor- ben   hast   durch
crown be mine, That   through Thy bit- ter death   Thou

163

dei- nen her- ben, bit- tern Tod. Das bitt' ich dich, mein
gain- edst, O Lord Christ, for me For this, for this, I

Herr und Gott!
cry to Thee!

No. 141   WARUM BETRÜBST DU DICH, MEIN HERZ

(B.W. XXXIX, p. 266)

Hymn attributed to Hans Sachs c. 1560   Melody by Monoetius 1565
Translation by Catherine Winkworth

Wa-   rum be- trübst du dich, mein Herz, be-
Why   art thou thus cast down, my heart? Why

164

küm- merst dich und trä- gest Schmerz nur um das zeit- lich'
trou- bled, why dost mourn a- part, O'er nought but earth- ly

Gut? Ver- trau' du dei- nem Her- ren Gott, der
wealth? Trust in thy God, be not a- fraid, He

al- le Ding' er- schaf- fen hat.
is thy Friend who all things made.

WARUM SOLLT' ICH MICH DENN GRÄMEN
Christmas Oratorio (B.W. V², p. 124)

Hymn by Paul Gerhardt 1653
Translation by Catherine Winkworth

Melody by J.G. Ebeling 1666

Ich will dich mit Fleiss be- wah- ren, ich will
Thee, dear Lord, with heed I'll cher- ish, Live to

dir le- ben hier, dir will ich ab- fah- ren. Mit dir
Thee, And with Thee Dy- ing shall not per- ish; But shall

will ich end- lich schwe- ben, vol- er Freud',
dwell with Thee for ev- er, Far on high,

oh- ne Zeit dort im an- dern Le- ben.
In the joy That can al- ter nev- er.

No. 143   WAS GOTT THUT, DAS IST WOHLGETHAN

Cantata 69 Iobe den Herrn, meine Seele (B.W. XVI, p. 379)

Hymn by Samuel Rodigast 1675   Melody from Nürnbergisches Gesang-Buch 1690
Translation by Catherine Winkworth

* Chord third appears in the instrumental accompaniment.

167

Cantata 144 Nimm, was dein ist. (B. W. XXX, p. 92)

Hymn by Albrecht, Markgraf of Brandenburg-Culmbach c. 1554
Translation by John S. Dwight   Melody of Secular song Il me suffit de
                                                 tous mes maulx c. 1530

Was   mein Gott will, das g'sheh' all- zeit, sein   Wil- le ist
Zu   hel- fen den'n er ist be- reit, die   an   ihn glau-
Now   may   the will of   God be- done! His   will I   would
His   help is   near to   ev'- ry   one, Let   not our cour-

- der be-   ste.   Er   hilft   aus   Noth, -
- ben fe-   ste.   In   all   our   need -
- not al-   ter.
- age fal-   ter.

- der   from- me Gott, und züch- ti-   get   mit Maa-
-, Our Friend in- deed, How ten- der-   ly   He   chid-

ssen.
eth!: Wer   Gott   ver- traut, fest   auf   ihn   baut, den
        To   Him   hold fast; He   builds to   last, Who

will   er   nicht   -   ver- las-   sen.
still in   God   -   con- fid-   eth..

No. 145   WAS MEIN GOTT WILL, DAS GESCHEH' ALLZEIT

St. Matthew Passion (B.W. IV, p. 83)

Hymn by Albrecht, Markgraf of Brandenburg-Culmbach c. 1554
Translation by John S. Dwight   Melody of secular song Il me suffit de
                                             tous mes maulx c. 1530

Was mein Gott will, das g'scheh' allzeit, sein. will' der   ist der
Zu   hel- fen den'n er   ist be- reit, die an   ihn glau- ben
Now may   the will of   God be- done! His will I   would not
His help is   near to   ev'- ry one, Let not   our cour- age

be ste;   er hilft aus Noth, der from- me Gott, und
fe- ste;
al- ter.   In all our need, Our Friend in- deed, How
fal- ter.

züch- ti- get mit   Maa-   ssen.   Wer Gott ver- traut, fest
ten- der- ly He   chid-   eth!! To Him hold fast: He

auf ihn baut, den   will er nicht ver-   las-   sen.
builds to last, Who   still in God con-   fid-   eth.

No. 146   WELT, ADE! ICH BIN DEIN MÜDE

Cantata 27 Wer weiss, wie nahe mir mein Ende (B.W. v¹, p. 244)

Hymn by Johann Albinus 1649   Melody by Johann Rosenmüller 1649
Translation by Catherine Winkworth

Welt, a- de! Welt, a-de!   ich bin dein   mü-   de, ich will
World, fare-well!.World, farewell! Of thee I'm   tir-   ed, Now t'ward

nach ich will nach dem   Him-   mel   zu,   da wird sein der
heav'n, Now 'tward heav'n my way   I   take;   There is   peace the

rech- te Frie-   de und die ew'-   ge, stol-   ze
long- de-sir-   ed, Lof-ty calm   that nought can

171

Ruh.   Welt, bei dir ist   Krieg   und Streit,   nichts, denn lau-ter
break: World with thee is   war   and strife,   Thou with cheat-ing

Ei-   tel-keit;   in   dem   Him-   mel   al-   le-
hopes   are rife,   But   in   heav'n   is   no   al-

zeit   Frie-   de,   Freud'   und See-   lig-
loy,   On-   ly   peace   and love   and

keit.
joy.

WENN MEIN STÜNDLEIN VORHANDEN IST

(B.W. XXXIX, p. 270)

Hymn by Nicolaus Herman 1562   Melody from Württemberg Gross Kirchen Gesangbuch 1596
Translation by Catherine Winkworth

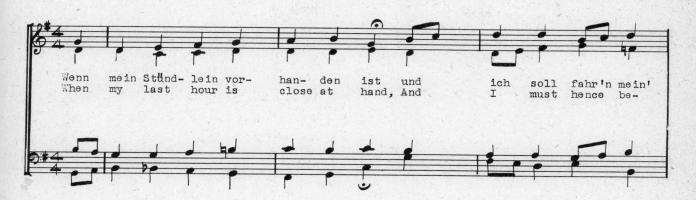

Wenn mein Stünd-lein vor- han- den ist und ich soll fahr'n mein'
When my last hour is close at hand, And I must hence be-

Stra- sse, so g'leit' du mich, Herr Je- su Christ, mit
take me, So Do Thou, Lord Je- sus, by me stand, Nor

Hülf' mich nicht ver- las- se: mein' Seel' an mei- nem
let Thine aid for- sake me; To Thy blest hands I

letz-   ten   End' be-   fehl' ich, Herr, in   dei-   ne Hand', du
now   com- mend My   soul, at this my   earth-   ly end, And

wirst sie wohl be-   wah- - -   ren.
Thou wilt safe- ly   keep   it.

No. 148   WENN WIR IN HÖCHSTEN NÖTHEN SEIN

(B.W. XXXIX, p. 272)

Hymn by Paul Eber c. 1560   Melody by **Louis Bourgeois** 1547
Translation by Catherine Winkworth

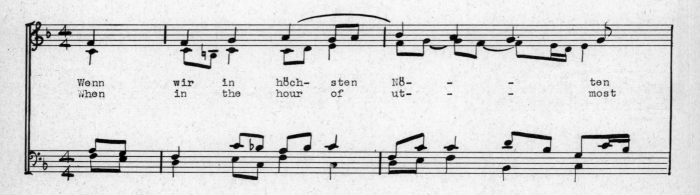

Wenn   wir in   höch- sten Nö- - -   ten
When   in   the hour of   ut- - -   most

sein   und   wis- sen   nicht, wo   aus und ein, und
need   We   know not   where to   look for aid, When

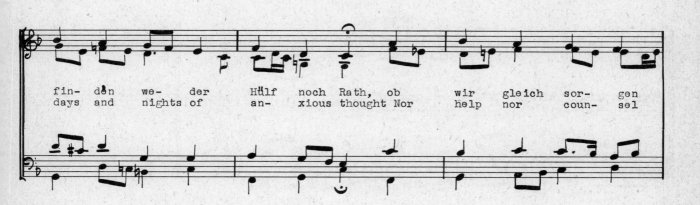

fin- den   we- der   Hülf noch Rath, ob   wir   gleich sor-   gen
days and   nights of an-   xious thought Nor help nor   coun-   sel

früh und   spat.
yet have brought.

175

Cantata 179 Siehe zu, dass deine Gottesfurcht nicht Heuchelei sei (B.W. XXXV, p. 292)

Hymn by Christoph Tietze c. 1663
Translation Cento

Melody by Georg Neumark 1641

Hymn by Georg Neumark 1641   Melody by Georg Neumark 1641
Translation by Catherine Winkworth

Wer   nur   den   lie- ben   Gott lässt wal-   ten und   hol- fet
den   wird er   wun- der- bar   er-   hal-   ten in   al- lem
If   thou but   suf- fer   God   to   guide   thee, And   hope in
He'll give thee strength what-e'er be- tide   thee, And   bear thee

auf   ihn   al-   le-   zeit,   Wer   Gott dem   al-   ler-
Kreuz und   Trau- rig- keit.   Who   trust in   God's un-
Him   through all thy   ways,
through the e-   vil   days.

höch-   sten traut, der   hat   auf   kei- nen   Sand ge- baut.
chang-   ing love Builds on   the   rock that   nought can movo.

177

* Hymn by Georg Neumark 1641
Translation by Catherine Winkworth   Melody by Georg Neumark 1641

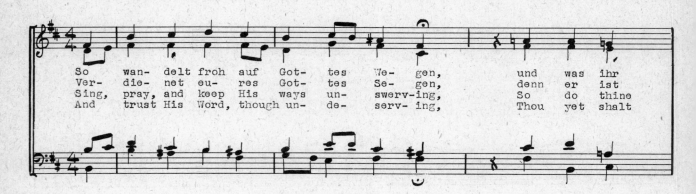

So   wan- delt froh auf Got- tes   We- gen,   und   was ihr
Ver- die- net eu- res Got- tes   Se- gen,   denn er ist
Sing, pray, and keep His ways un- swerv-ing,   So   do thine
And   trust His Word, though un- de- serv-ing,   Thou yet shalt

thut, das thut ge-   treu!   denn wel- cher sei- ne
al-   le   Mor- gen   neu: God   nev- er   yet   for-
own   part faith-ful- ly,   God   nev- er   yet   for-
find it   true for   thee;

Zu-   ver-sicht auf Gott setzt, den ver- lässt er   nicht.
sook at need The soul that trust- ed   Him in- deed.

* Bach's text differs from the original.

178

WERDE MUNTER MEIN GEMÜTE

St. Matthew Passion (B.W. IV, p. 173)

Hymn by Johann Rist 1642
Translation by John S. Dwight

Melody by Johann Schop 1642

Cantata 172 Erschallet, ihr Lieder (B.W. XXXV, p. 69)

Hymn by Philipp Nicolai 1597
Translation by Catherine Winkworth

Melody adapted by Philipp Nicolai 1599

Von   Gott kommt mir ein   Freu-den-schein, wenn du mit dei-   nen
O   Herr Je- su, mein   trau-tes Gut,   dein Wort, dein Geist, dein
But   if Thou look on   me   in love,   There straightways falls from
Thy   word and Spir-it,   flesh and blood, Re- fresh my   soul with

Au- ge- lein mich   freund-lich thust an- bli-   cken.
Leib und Blut mich in- ner- lich er- qui-   cken.
God a-   bove A   ray of pur- est plea-   sure;
heaven-ly food, Thou art my hid- den trea-   sure;

Nimm mich   freund-lich   in   dein' Ar- me,   dass ich war- me
Let Thy   grace Lord,   Warm and   cheer me. O   draw near me;

werd' von Gna-   den: Auf dein Wort komm' ich ge- la-   den.
Thou hast taught   us   Thee to   seek since Thou hast sought us!

* Chord third appears in instrumental accompaniment.

Cantata 40 Dazu ist erschienen der Sohn Gottes (B.W. VII, p. 377)

Hymn by Caspar Fuger 1592
Translation by Catherine Winkworth

Melody from Dresden Gesangbuch 1593

Die Stünd' macht Leid, die Stünd' macht Leid; Christus bringt Freud', weil
Sin brought us grief, Sin brought us grief, but Christ relief, When

er zu Trost in diese Welt gekommen. Mit
down to earth He came for our salvation; Since

uns ist Gott nun in der Noth: wer ist, der uns als
God with us is dwelling thus, Who dares to speak the

Christen kann verdammen?
Christians condemnation?

Hymn by Christoph Runge 1653
Translation by J. Troutbeck

Melody from Dresden Gesangbuch 1593

Seid froh, die- weil, seid froh, die- weil dass eu- er Heil ist
Re- joice and sing! Re- joice and sing! Your gra- cious King. As

hie ein Gott und auch ein Mensch ge- bo- ren, der
man is born, and lays a- side His glo- ry; He

wel- cher ist der Herr und Christ in Da- vids Stadt, von
is a- dor'd As Christ and Lord, And ev- 'ry tongue re-

Vie- len aus- er- ko- ren.
peats the won- drous sto- ry.

Hymn by Martin Luther 1524   Melody from Klug's Geistliche Lieder 1535
Translation by Richard Massie

183

No. 1

ALLENA GUD I HIMMELRIK   (24B)

(Allein Gott in der Höh sei Ehr)

Hymn adapted by Decius 1525
Translation by Catherine Winkworth

Melody from Schumann's Geistliche Lieder 1539

All glo- ry be   to   Thee,   Most   High,   To

Thee   all a-   dor- a- -   tion!   In

grace   and   truth   Thou   draw- est   nigh   To

184

of- fer us - sal- va- - tion. Thou

show- est Thy good will to men, And

peace shall reign on earth a- gain; We

praise Thy Name for- ev- er.

Hymn by F.M. Franzen c. 1814   Melody from Klug's Geistliche Lieder 1535
Translation by P.M. Lindberg

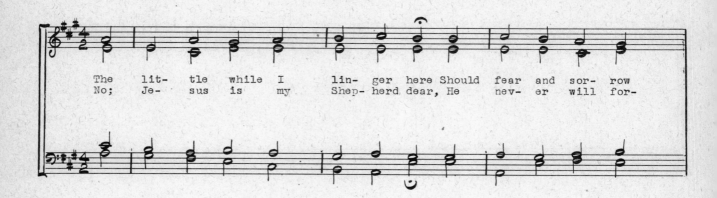

The lit- tle while I lin- ger here Should fear and sor- row
No; Je- sus is my Shep- herd dear, He nev- er will for-

fret me?   He gave His life His flock to save, His
get me.

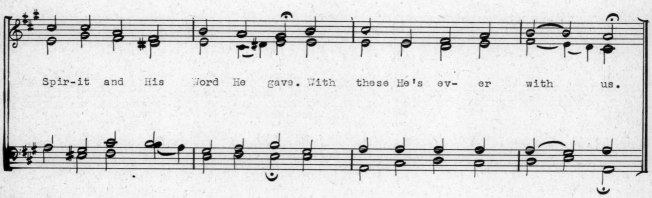

Spir-it and His Word He gave. With these He's ev- er with us.

L86

No. 3   DITT HUFVUD, JESU! BÖJES   (91)

(O Haupt voll Blut und Wunden)

Hymn by Paul Gerhardt 1656   Melody by Melchior Teschner 1613
Translation by J.W. Alexander

O sa- cred head now wound- ed,   With grief and

shame weighed down,   Now scorn- ful- ly sur- round- ed,

With thorns Thine on- ly crown!   Once reigning

in the high- est   In light and   maj- es-   ty,   Dis-

hon- ored now Thou di- est,   Yet   here I   wor- ship Thee.

No. 4   EN DAG SKALL UPPGÅ FÖR VÅR SYN   (498)

Hymn by Bartholomäus Ringwaldt c. 1565   Melody from Koralbok 1697
Translation by P.A. Peter

The   day   is   sure- ly   draw- ing   near,   When
Will with great maj- es-   ty ap-   pear,   As

He, the Lord's A-   noint-   ed,   No   more the
Judge of   all   ap-   point-   ed.

gos- pel   call is   heard   To   turn from   sin and

heed God's Word: The day of   grace is   end-   ed.

189

No. 5   EN STJERNA GICK PÅ HIMLEN FRAM   (67A)

(Puer natus in Bethlehem)

14th Century Latin hymn   Melody from Lossius' Psalmodia 1553
Translation anonymous

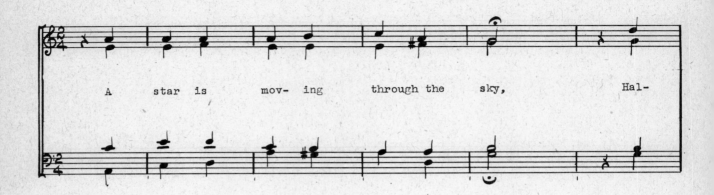

A star is mov- ing through the sky,   Hal-

le- lu- ia!   Be- fore the wise men, won- drous-

ly.   Hal- le- lu- ia! Hal- le- lu- ia!

190

No. 6   GUD HAR AF SIN BARMHERTIGHET   (144)

(Es ist das Heil uns kommen her)

Hymn by Paul Speratus 1523
Translation by G.T. Rygh

Melody from Etlich Christlich Lyeder 1524

He   that be- lieves and   is bap- tized   Shall
Bap- tized in- to   the   death of Christ,   He

see   the   Lord's sal- va-   tion;   Through Christ's re-
is   a   new   cre- a-   tion;

demp-tion he   shall   stand   A-   mong   the   glo- rious

heaven-ly band   Of   ev- 'ry   tribe and   na-   tion.

191

Hymn by Martin Luther 1524   Melody from Walter's Geistliche Gesangk Buchleyn 1524
Translation by Richard Massie

May   God   be   praised hence- forth and   blest for-   ev-   er!
With   His   own   flesh   and   blood our   souls doth   nour- ish;

Who   Him- self both   gift   and   giv- er,   Oh,   Lord, have
May   they   grow there- by   and   flour-ish!

mer- cy   on   us.   By   Thy   ho- ly   bod- y, Lord, the

same   Which from   Thine own   moth- er   Ma-   ry

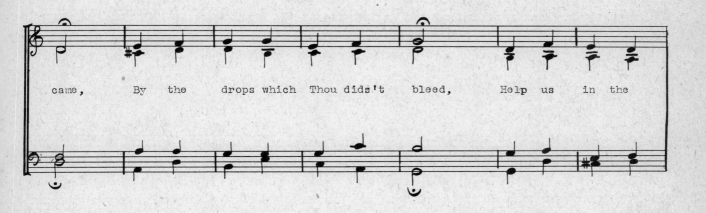

came, By the drops which Thou dids't bleed, Help us in the

hour of need. Oh Lord, have mer- cy on us.

No. 8   I HOPPET SIG MIN FRÄLSTA SJÄL FÖRNÖJER   (487)

Hymn by Elle Andersdatter c. 1645   Melody from 17th century
Translation by G.H. Trabert

In   hope   my   soul,   re- deemed   to   bliss un-   end- ing,
To heav- en's glo- rious height by   faith as-   cend- ing,

Is mind- ful ev- er That Christ did sev- er

The bonds of death, that I might live for- ev- er.

No. 9   KOM HELGE ANDE! HERRE GOD   (133)

Hymn by Martin Luther 1524   Melody from Walter's Geistliche gesangk Buchleyn 1524
Translation by C.W. Foss

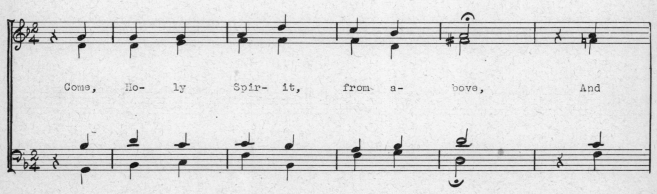

Come, Ho- ly Spir- it, from a- bove, And

194

kin- dle   in   our   hearts Thy   love;   In   all   our

dark- ness   on   us   shine,   **And**   fill   us   with   Thy

grace di-   vine,   And   fill   us   with Thy   grace di-   vine.

(Gelobet seist du Jesu Christ)

Hymn by Martin Luther 1524
Translation by A. T. Russell

Melody from Walter's Geistliche Gesangk Buchleyn 1524

196

Hymn by P. Hegelund 1586
Translation by O.T. Sanden

Melody c. 1542

De- spair not, O   heart, in   thy   sor- row, But

hope from God's prom-is- es   bor- row;   Be-

ware, in thy   sor- row, of   sin- ning,   For

death is of   life   the be-   gin- ning.

197

(Es woll' uns Gott genädig sein)

Hymn by Olaus Petri c. 1552   Melody from Strassburger Kirchenamt 1525
Translation by Augustus Nelson

Our   Fa- ther,   mer- ci-   ful and   good,   Who
Oh!   cleanse us   in   our   Sav- iour's blood,   And

dost to   Thee in- vite   us,   Send   un- to
to   Thy- self u- nite   us.

us Thy ho- ly   Word,   And   let it   guide us

ev-   er;   Then   in   this   world   of   dark- ness,

Lord,   Shall   naught from   Thee us   sev-   er:

Grant   us,   O   Lord, this   fa-   vor!

Hymn by J. Svedberg c. 1735   Melody from Koralbok 1697
Translation anonymous

'Tis   fin-   ished! So   the   Sav- iour   cried,   And

meek- ly   bowed His   head   and   died: 'Tis   fin- ished!

yes,   the   race' is   run,   The   bat- tle   fought, the vict'ry won.

Hymn by J. O. Wallin 1839
Translation by Felix Hanson

Melody from Walter's Geystliche Gesangk Buchleyn 1524

The eyes of Je-sus see a- gain, And dark- ness
Death seeks to hold that life in vain, That once för

now is driv- en. Je- sus from the tomb comes nigh
us was giv- en.

With Res- ur- rec- tion ban- nered high   Pro- claim- ing

life e- ter- nal.   Hal- le- lu- jah!

201

(In dulci jubilo)

Hymn by J.O. Wallin 1839   Melody from Klug's Geistliche Lieder 1535
Translation by A.T. Russell

Now   sing we,   now re-   joice -   -;   Now

raise   to   heaven our   voice -   -;   Lo!

He   from   whom   joy   stream-   eth, Poor

in   the   man-   ger   lies -   -;   Yet

not   so   bright- ly   beam-   eth   The

sun   in   yon-   der   skies   -   -!

Thou   my   Sav-   iour   art   -!

Thou   my   Sav-   iour   art!

Hymn by Fortunatus c. 609
Transcribed by Wallin
Translation by Augustus Nelson

Melody from Koralbok 1697

Praise the Sav- iour   Now and   ev-   er!   Praise Him   all be-
Pros- trate ly- ing,   Suf- f'ring, dy-   ing   On the   cross, a

neath the   skies!   Vic- t'ry gain- ing,   Life ob-   tain- ing,
Sac- ri-   fice;

Now   in glo-   ry   He doth   rise.

204

(Wie schön leuchtet der Morgenstern)

Hymn by J.O. Wallin 1839
Translation by E.W. Olson

Melody adapted by Philipp Nicolai 1599

All hail to thee, O bles- sed morn!
O sa- cred and im- mor- tal day,

To ti- dings
When un- to

long by pro- phets borne
earth, in glo- rious ray,

Hast thou ful- fill- ment giv-
De- scends the grace of heav-

en.
en!

Sing- ing, Ring- ing   Sounds are blend- ing, Prais- es send- ing

Un- to heav- en For the Sav- iour to us giv- en.

(Nun komm der Heiden Heiland)

Hymn by Martin Luther 1524   Melody from Erfurter Enchiridion 1524
Translation by W.M. Reynolds

Come, Thou Sav- iour of   our   race,   Choic- est Gift   of

heav'- nly   grace!   O   Thou bless- ed   Vir- gin's Son,

Be   Thy race on   earth be- gun.

Hymn by J.O. Wallin 1816
Translation Cento

Melody from Rostockerhandboken 1529

Je- ho- vah, Thee we glo- ri- fy, Ru-

ler up- on Thy throne on high! O let Thy

Word Thro' all the earth be heard. Ho- ly, ho-

ly, ho- ly art Thou, O Lord.

(Ein' feste Burg ist unser Gott)

Hymn by Martin Luther 1527
Translation Cento

Melody by Martin Luther 1527

A   might- y   For- tress is   our   God,   A
He   helps us   in   our   ev- 'ry   need   That

trust- y Shield and   Weap-   -   on,   The -   old ma-
hath us now   o'er- tak-   -   en.

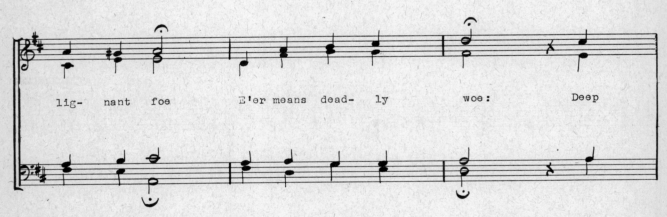

lig- nant foe   E'er means dead- ly   woe: Deep

208

guile and cru- el might   Are   his   dread   arms   in

fight,   On   earth   is   not   his   e-   qual.

No. 21   VÅR HERRAS JESU KRISTI DÖD (154)

(Mein Seel, o Herr, muss loben dich)

Hymn by Haguin Spegel 1686   Melody by Bartholomäus Gesius 1601
Translation by Olaf Olson

The   death   of   Je-   sus   Christ, our   Lord,   We

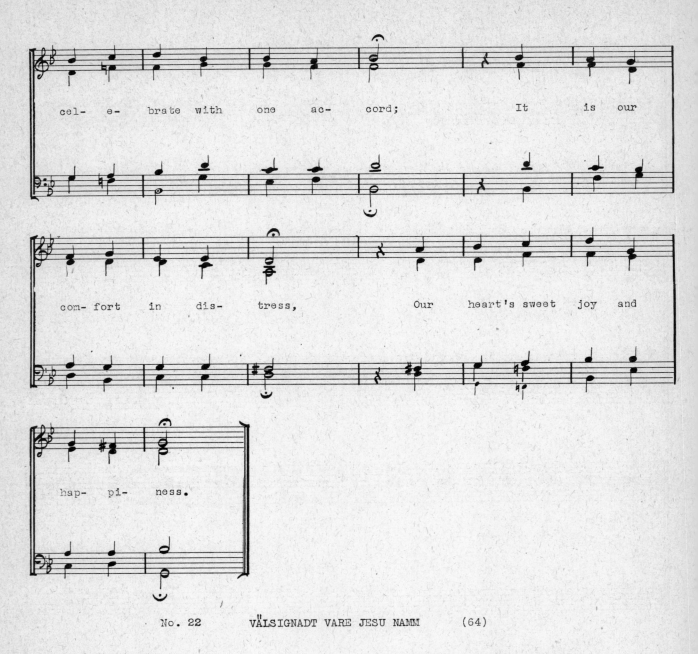

cel- e- brate with one ac- cord; It is our

com- fort in dis- tress, Our heart's sweet joy and

hap- pi- ness.

No. 22   VÄLSIGNADT VARE JESU NAMM   (64)

Hymn by J. Åström   Melody from Swedish Psalmbok 1567
Translation by Felix Hanson

Praised   be   our   bless- ed   Sav- iour's   name,   And
A   safe   re- treat   it   will   re- main   To

NORWEGIAN CHORALES
1-20

No. 1   AKK HERRE GUD (2b)

Hymn by Johann Major 1613
Translation by Catherine Winkworth

Melody from As hymnodus sacer 1625

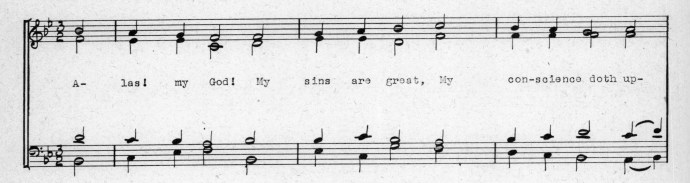

A- las! my God! My sins are great, My con-science doth up-

braid me; And now I find That at my strait No

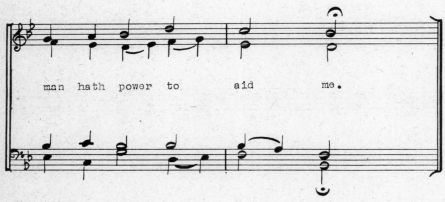

man hath power to aid me.

212

ALENE GUD I HIMMERIK (5)

(Allein Gott in der Höh sei Ehr)

Hymn adapted by Nicolaus Decius 1525
Translation by Catherine Winkworth

Melody from Schumann's Geistliche Lieder 1539

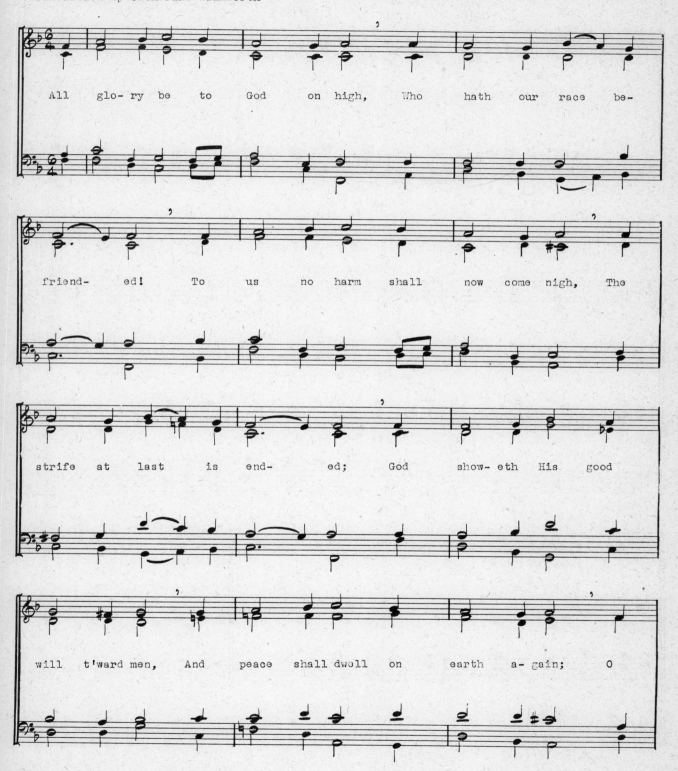

All glo-ry be to God on high, Who hath our race be-

friend- ed! To us no harm shall now come nigh, The

strife at last is end- ed; God show- eth His good

will t'ward men, And peace shall dwell on earth a- gain; O

thank   Him   for   His   good-   ness!

No. 3   AV HÖIHETEN   (12)

(Wie schön leuchtet der Morgenstern)

Hymn by Philipp Nicolai 1597   Melody adapted by Philipp Nicolai 1599
Translation by B.J. Palmer

The   Morn- ing   Star up-   on   us   gleams; How   full   of   grace   and

truth His beams, How pass- ing fair His   splen- dor!   Good

214

Shep- herd, Da- vid's prop- er heir, My King in heaven, Thou

dost me bear Up- on Thy bos- om ten- der.

Near- est, Dear- est, High- est, bright-est, Thou de- light-est

Still to love me, Thou, so high en- throned a- bove me.

215

Hymn by L.A. Gotler 1714   Melody by L.M. Lindeman c. 1871
Translation by Jane Borthwick

Sav- iour of sinners now re- vive us   With Thy free mer- cy   from a-

bove;   Friend of the sin-ful and the wea- ry,   Turn un- to   us   Thy

heart   of   love!   O   come, Thy sweet com-pas-sion

show- ing,   On   our poor souls Thy grace be- stow- ing.

216

DEN HERRE KRIST I DÖDENS BÅND (18A)

(Christ lag in Todesbanden)

Hymn by Martin Luther 1524
Translation by Richard Massie

Melody from Walter's Geystliche Gesangk Buchleyn 1524

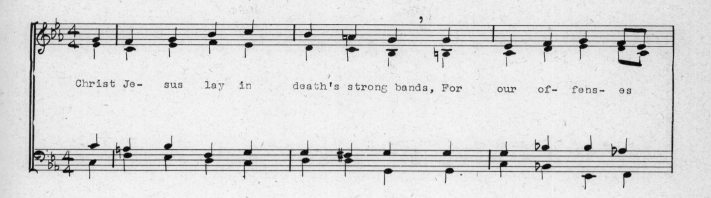

Christ Je- sus lay in death's strong bands, For our of- fens- es

giv- en; But now at God's right hand He stands, And

brings us life from heav- en: Where- fore let us

joy- ful be And sing to God right thank- ful- ly Loud

songs of Hal- le- lu- jah! Hal- le- lu- jah!

No. 6   DET HEV EI ROSA SPRUNGE (26)

(Es ist ein Ros entsprungen)

15th or 16th Century Twelfth Night Carol   Melody from Kölnischer Gesangbuch 1599
Translation anonymous

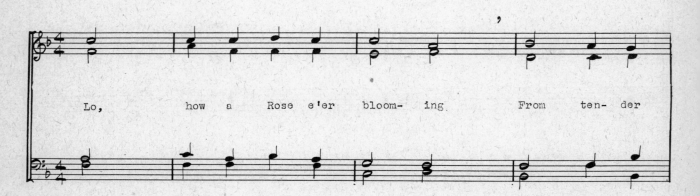

Lo,   how a Rose e'er bloom- ing   From ten- der

stem hath sprung! Of Jes- se's lin- eage com- ing

As men of old have sung. It came, a flow'r-et

bright, A- mid the cold of win- ter,

When half spent was the night.

(Gelobet seist du Jesu Christ)

Hymn by Martin Luther 1524   Melody from Walter's Geistliche gesangk Buchleyn 1524
Translation by A.T. Russell

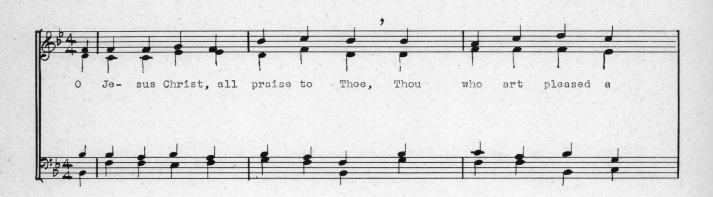

O Je- sus Christ, all praise to Thee, Thou who art pleased a

man to be; To dwell with men Thou dost not scorn, And

ang- els shout to see Thee born, Hal- le- lu- ja.

(Puer natus in Bethlehem)

14th Century Latin hymn   Melody from Lossius' Psalmodia 1553
Translation by Philip Schaff

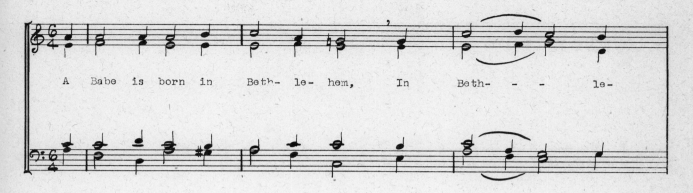

A Babe is born in Beth- le- hem,   In   Beth- - - le-

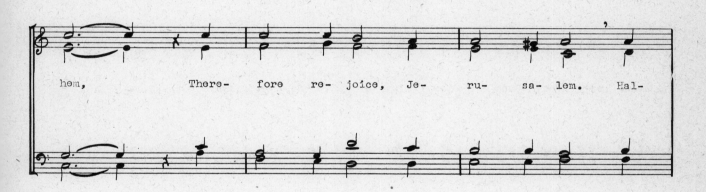

hem,   There- fore re- joice, Je- ru- sa- lem. Hal-

le- lu- ja, hal- le- - - lu- ja!

(Vom Himmel hoch)

Hymn by Martin Luther 1535   Melody from Schumann's Geistliche Lieder 1539
Translation by Catherine Winkworth

From heaven a- bove to earth I come To bear good news to

ev- ery home; Glad ti- dings of great joy I bring, Where-

of I now will say and sing.

(Herr ich habe misgehandelt)

Hymn by Johann Franck 1649   Melody by Johann Crüger 1649
Translation by Catherine Winkworth

Lord, to Thee I make con- fes- sion, I have sinned and

gone a- stray, I have mul- ti- plied trans- gres- sion,

Chos- en for my- self my way: Forced at last to

see my er- rors, Lord, I trem- ble at Thy ter- ors.

HVO ENE LADER HERREN RÅDE   (32⸱)

(Wer nur den lieben Gott lässt walten)

Hymn by Georg Neumark 1641   Melody by Georg Neumark 1641
Translation by Catherine Winkworth

If   Thou but suf- fer   God   to   guide thee,   And

hope   in   Him through all   thy ways,   He'll give thee

strength what-e'er be- tide   thee,   And   bear   thee through the

e- vil days; Who trusts in God's un- chang- ing

love Builds on the rock that naught can move.

No. 12   **JEG SYNGER JULEKVAD**   (119)

(In dulci jubilo)

15th Century Latin Hymn   Melody from Klug's Geistliche Lieder 1535
Translation by A.T. Russell

Now sing we, now re- joice,   Now raise to heaven our

voice; Lo! He from whom joy stream- eth, Poor

in the man- ger lies; Yet not so bright- ly

beam- eth The sun in yon- der skies!

Thou my Sav- iour art! Thou my Sav- iour art!

(Liebster Jesu wir sind hier)

Hymn by T. Clausnitzer 1663   Melody from Ahle's Sonntagsandachten 1664
Translation by Catherine Winkworth

Bless- ed Je- sus,   at Thy word   We are gath- ered

all to hear Thee; Let our hearts and souls be stirred

Now to seek and love and fear Thee; By Thy teach- ings

sweet and ho- ly Drawn from earth to love Thee sole- ly.

Hymn by N.F.S. Grundtvig 1857
Translation by C. Doving

Melody by L.H. Lindeman 1840

Built on the   Rock   the   Church   doth   stand,

E- ven when stee- ples are fall-   ing;

Crumb- led have have spires   in   ev-   ery   land.

228

Bells still are chim- ing and call- ing;

Call- ing the young and old to rest,

But a- bove all the soul dis- trest,

Long- ing for rest ev- er- last- ing.

(Komm, Gott Schöpfer, heiliger Geist)

Hymn by Martin Luther 1524   Melody from Klug's Geistliche Lieder 1535
Translation by Richard Massie

Come, Ho- ly Spir-it, God and Lord! Be   all Thy gra- ces

now out- poured On   each be- liev- er's soul and heart; Thy

fer- vent love to   them im- part.

230

No. 16   LOVER DEN HERRE   (152)

(Lobe den Herren)

Hymn by J. Neander 1680
Translation by Catherine Winkworth

Melody from Stralsund Gesangbuch 1665

Praise to the Lord, the Al- might- y, the King of cre-

a- tion! O my soul, praise Him, for

He is thy health and sal- va- tion!

All ye who hear, Now to His tem- ple draw

near,   Join me in   glad a- do- ra-   tion.

No. 17   MIN SJEL OG ÅND, OPMUNTRE DIG   (165B)

Hymn by J.N. Brun 1786   Melody from Thomissöns Psalmebog 1569
Translation by O.H. Smeby

How blest are they who   hear God's word, And   keep and heed what

they have heard: They   wis- dom dai- ly   gath-   er; Their

light shines bright- er day by day, And   while   they tread life's

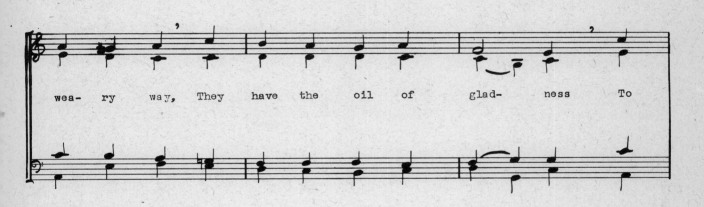

wea- ry way, They have the oil of glad- ness To

soothe their pain and sad- ness.

Hymn by M.B. Landstad 1855   Melody is a Sequence from the ancient Olavs-fest in Nidaros
Translation by O.T. Sanden

Dark- ness o'er the earth is steal- ing In my lone- ly

cham- ber kneel- ing, I will say my even- ing prayer,

Long- ing for a clos- er un- ion, With my God I

hold com- mun- ion And com- mit me to His care.

(Herzlich thut mich verlangen)

Hymn by Paul Gerhardt 1656   Melody by Hans Leo Hassler 1601
Translation by J.W. Alexander

O sa- cred head now   wound- ed,   With   grief and   shame weighed

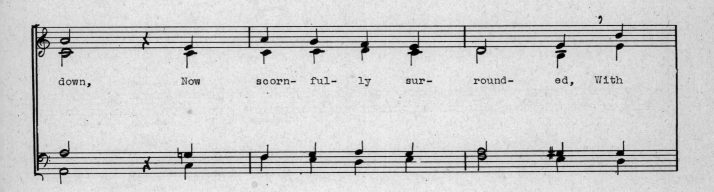

down,   Now   scorn- ful- ly sur-   round- ed, With

thorns Thine on- ly   crown!   Once   reign- ing in the

high- est In light and maj- es- ty, Dis-

hon- ored now Thou di- est, Yet here I wor-ship Thee.

No. 20   O FADER VAR I HIMMERIK   (181)

(Vater unser im Himmelreich)

Hymn by Martin Luther 1539   Melody from Schumann's Geistliche Lieder 1539
Translation by Catherine Winkworth

Our Fa- ther, Thou in heaven a- bove, Who bid- dest us to

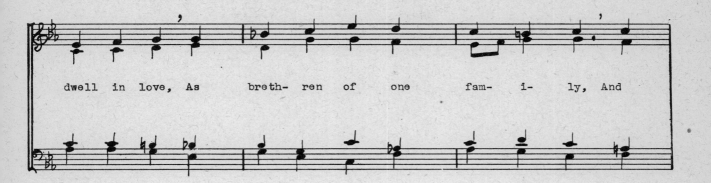

dwell in love, As breth- ren of one fam- i- ly, And

cry for all we need to Thee; Teach us to mean the

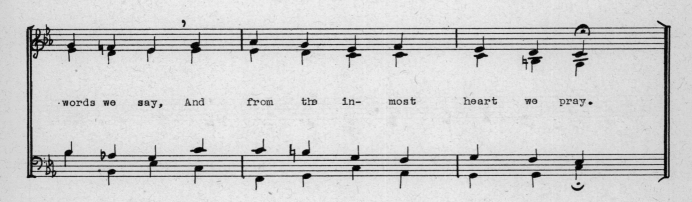

words we say, And from the in- most heart we pray.

237